| DATE LOANED | BORROWER'S NAME | DATE RETURNED |
|---|---|---|
| | | |
| | | |
| | | |
| | | |

# PROBLEMS OF MORPHOGENESIS IN CILIATES

*The Kinetosomes in Development, Reproduction and Evolution*

# PROBLEMS OF MORPHOGENESIS IN CILIATES

## *The Kinetosomes in Development, Reproduction and Evolution*

**André Lwoff**
HEAD OF THE DEPARTMENT
OF MICROBIAL PHYSIOLOGY
INSTITUT PASTEUR, PARIS

**1950**
**John Wiley & Sons, Inc., New York**
**Chapman & Hall, Limited, London**

PRINTED IN THE UNITED STATES OF AMERICA

*"Il y a lieu de se flatter que ces découvertes produiront plusieurs bons effets. Elles doivent naturellement nous jeter dans une grande défiance à l'égard de ces règles générales, auxquelles, si je puis parler ainsi, on a prétendu borner la nature et qui ne peuvent servir qu'à mettre obstacle à nos connaissances."*

A. Trembley, "Mémoires pour servir à l'histoire d'un genre de Polype d'eau douce à bras en forme de cornes." J. et H. Verbeeck, éd. Leiden, 1744.

# Foreword

The author had the privilege of delivering the Dunham lectures at Harvard University during the academic year 1947–1948. One of the lectures, given under the title "Visible self-reproducing cytoplasmic granules in the life cycle of some parasitic ciliates," is the nucleus around which the book has been built.

It was not possible, in the course of one lecture, to discuss, or even to mention, all the aspects of the problems raised by the ciliates. The author has therefore been pleased to take the opportunity kindly offered by Doctors Goddard, Schmitt, and Weiss, as advisory editors of the Wiley Biological Research Series, of organizing some of these problems into this monograph. He was especially pleased because many of the data related to ciliates are in perfect agreement with the theoretical conceptions of Dr. Paul Weiss, chairman of the Advisory Board, concerning what he has called "molecular ecology."

This monograph is not a treatise. No attempt is made to cover all the aspects of the subject or to give an exhaustive survey of the literature. The author's work on the morphology and biology of the ciliates started in 1921 and extended over many years. Having for some time followed other roads, he has, nevertheless, the impression that a somewhat aged and matured knowledge of the ciliates is not without advantages. Ciliates are very nice animals indeed, but, like other delicate creatures, they have to be treated with a buffered and balanced mixture of love and experience.

The author expresses the hope that his American friends, to whom this book is dedicated, will find some austere pleasure in reading these pages, or, at least, in looking at the pictures.

The difficulties which may be encountered by some Anglo-Saxon readers may not necessarily result from inadequate knowledge of their own language. They could be due in part to the fact that the French author, owing to a certain distrust of translations, has, despite his diffidence, written this book directly in English.

The author is indebted to his friends E. Fauré-Frémiet and Jacques Monod for helpful criticisms and discussions.

André Lwoff

*Paris, France*
*January, 1950*

The author wishes also to thank the editors of the *Archives de zoologie expérimentale et générale* for kind permission to reproduce Figs. 1 to 16, 19 (slightly modified) to 26, and 29. Figure 17 is taken from E. Chatton, A. and M. Lwoff, and J. Monod, *Compt. rend. soc. biol., 107* (1931); Fig. 18 from S. Villeneuve-Brachon, *Arch. zool. exp. et gén., 82* (1940); Fig. 27 from E. Chatton, A. and M. Lwoff, and L. Tellier, *Compt. rend. soc. biol., 100* (1929); Fig. 28 (slightly modified) from E. Fauré-Frémiet, *Bull. biol. France-Belgique, 79* (1945); Fig. 30 from E. Chatton and J. Seguela, *Bull. biol. France-Belgique, 74* (1940); Fig. 31 from E. Chatton and A. and M. Lwoff, *Compt. rend. soc. biol., 107* (1931); and Fig. 32 from E. Fauré-Frémiet and H. Mugard, *Compt. rend. acad. sci., 227* (1948).

# Contents

CHAPTER 1

# Introduction of the Kinetosome Considered as a Model of a Visible Cytoplasmic Unit Endowed with Genetic Continuity

Development of an animal is a complex process generally considered as the result of interactions between a specific protoplasm and hereditary outfit on the one hand, and a complex set of environmental factors on the other. The most important phenomena during this process are egg cleavage and subsequent cell multiplication, cell movements, differentiation, and modulation, the sum of which results in the formation of tissues, organs, and organism. Development is an epigenetic phenomenon. Starting from an egg, which is a highly complicated cell, every organism has to be elaborated at each generation. This is ontogenesis.

During development, different cell lines acquire different properties. Differentiation is the process resulting in specialization of a cell as evidenced by its distinctive actual and potential functions. It is by definition irreversible.

It is known that there is, in general, a marked antagonism between cell differentiation and cell division, that some highly specialized cells are unable to divide, that the development of an animal from an egg is, as a whole, an irreversible process, that evolution itself is irreversible. It is known also that the animal has, with a few exceptions, relegated to the germinal line the responsibility for the maintenance of the species.

But Protozoa are, as stated by C. Dobell (1911), "non-cellular" organisms. A cell is a differentiated part of an organism. Protozoa are complete individuals, whole organisms, and behave as such. If one wants to remark the fact that they generally have one nucleus, it is best to say that they are monoenergid.

The fundamental morphological and biochemical similarity of living beings makes it probable that some processes of morphogenesis, differentiation, and evolution in Protozoa must have something in common with the homologous processes in Metazoa.

How did the Protozoa, and especially the ciliates, manage to reconcile the non-cellular state with such processes as differentiation, development, morphogenesis, evolution, and reproduction, some of which are antagonistic and irreversible? This is our main problem. It will be discussed in terms of particulate phenomena.

Numerous data concerning development have led embryologists to the conclusion that cell differentiation must be attributed to the unequal distribution and segregation of specific particulate material. "During the development," writes R. Harrison (1937), "all movements, differentiation, and in fact all developmental processes are actually effected by the cytoplasm."

The importance of specific cytoplasmic units in the life of organisms and especially in developmental functions seems thus to be well recognized. Cytoplasm is not just a collection of enzymes or a plastic and complaisant receptor passively submitted to the dictatorship of genes, but certainly contains self-reproducing bodies endowed with specificity. And the geneticists have indeed concluded that some specific determinants do exist in the cytoplasm and play their role in heredity.

As a matter of fact, according to E. Caspari's review (1948), some twenty cases of cytoplasmic inheritance have already been described. Many of them deal with the properties of chloroplasts, absent in animals. The plasmagenes, theoretically necessary for development, are, so far, exceedingly rare in heredity. Their presence has not been demonstrated directly; they have not been seen; and they remain in the most irritating form of a logical hypothesis. It seems therefore of utmost importance for the progress of biology, and also of biochemistry, to develop this particulate conception of cytoplasm.

While discussing the problems of modulation and differentiation, Paul Weiss (1947) has tried to transcribe what he calls "the symbolic concepts of cells and protoplasm" in terms of molecular phenomena and has introduced the concept of "molecular ecology," according to which a cell is to be viewed as an organized mixed population of molecules and molecular groups.

Let us quote some of his propositions:

1. "Each population is made up of molecular species of very different composition, sizes, densities, rank, and stability, from trivial inorganic compounds to the huge and highly organized protein systems. Some segments of these populations occur in relatively constant 'symbiotic' groupings, often of a limited size range; these form the various particulates of the cell content.

2. "It is one of the fundamental characteristics of cellular organization that the various species constituting the population are not self-sufficient, but depend in various degrees upon other members of the population as well as upon the physical conditions prevailing in the space they occupy. Survival and orderly function of the total population are predicated on the presence of all essential members in definite concentrations, combinations, and distributions.

3. "In view of this intricate interdependence, given molecular species can exist, and given interactions between species can occur, only within a certain limited range of conditions specific for each kind. We might call these con-

ditions the 'existential and operational prerequisites' for each molecular species or group. The probability of members of a given species to persist, hence to be found, in any but the appropriate setting, would be extremely low.

4. "If the specific existential and operational prerequisites for the various molecular species and groups differ at different sites of the cell, different species will automatically become segregated into their appropriate ecological environments. As a result, even a wholly indiscriminate mixture can become sorted out into a definite space pattern. Certain species will assemble in relatively stable combinations, like biotic groups, while others, mutually incompatible, will separate."

This is a beautiful concept. But it is a theory. Is it possible to obtain some positive data concerning cytoplasmic units?

C. Darlington (1944) has classified all biological corpuscles into three categories: (1) the nuclear system; (2) the plastids of the green plants or corpuscular system; and (3) what he has described as the "undefined residues of heredity," not associated with any visible body; this is the "cytoplasmic" or "molecular" system whose constituents are generally known as "plasmagenes."

"In order that we should find out something more about these free plasmagenes," writes Darlington in his classical book, "we must try to form a more precise picture of how they live, move, and multiply. It seems likely that they are protein molecules or aggregates. Evidently, they are such that, like true genes, they can arise only from proteins of the same kind apart from mutations. Unlike true genes, however, their reproduction is not controlled by a mechanical equilibrium but will be subject rather to conditions of chemical equilibrium genotypically controlled but specific for each type of gene."

This is also an entirely hypothetical conception. When we study viruses or enzymes, we enjoy the criteria of infection, disease, and specific chemical reactions, and, of course, in some cases the control of electron microscopy. No identified chemical reaction has been ascribed to any plasmagene. How can we obtain a picture of the activity of plasmagenes? The situation seems difficult to say the least. But Nature does not like to be disregarded and rarely forgives classifications. Among these "undefined residues of heredity" which are considered as invisible are perfectly visible granules, cytoplasmic, specific, self-reproducing visible granules.

Thus we can approach directly the study of molecular ecology. It is of course very advantageous to deal with invisible particles. We may organize them at will without apparent danger. But what will happen to the theory, when, by chance, we are dealing with real visible granules, the life history of which we are able to analyze? As will be seen very soon, we are today in a position to perform this analysis. Thus, we will find that, although molecular ecology is a very clear, almost schematic, and very clever theoretical conception, it is nevertheless in excellent agreement with the facts. Such abnormal events happen from time to time. If Nature rarely forgives classification, she sometimes forgives theories.

In all animals or plants, at the base of each flagellum or cilium, one sees a spherical corpuscle. These corpuscles always reproduce themselves by division. They are "self-reproducing" systems, and obviously cytoplasmic. Shall we refer to them as "undefined residues of heredity" or as plasmagenes? Why should we? Let us simply call them by their name: "blepharoplasts" or "kinetosomes," and let us first say a few words about the way protozoologists consider these kinetosomes.

During cell division, a granule is present in the center of the aster, which is the centriole or central body. When spermiogenesis proceeds, the flagella arise from this centriole. The centriole of animal cells is a lineal descendant of the centriole of earlier cell generations, probably back to the egg.

In the flagellates, the flagellum arises from a granule

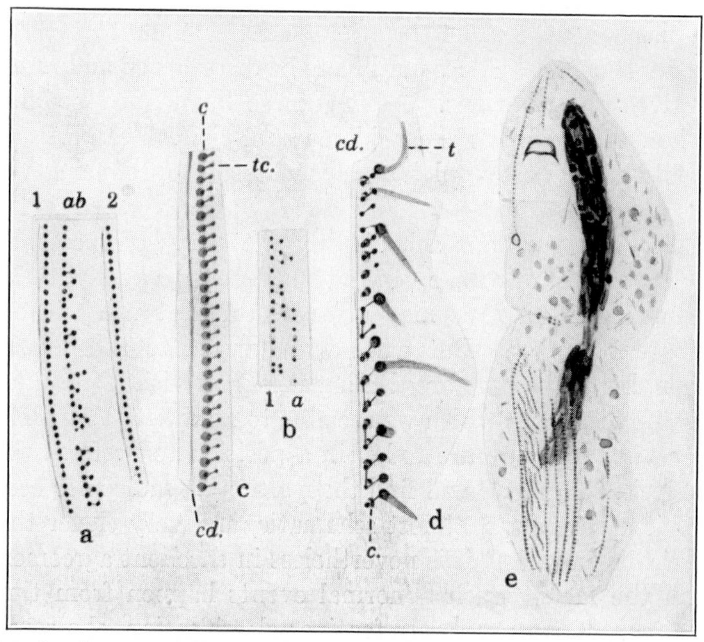


Fig. 1. Aspects of kinetosomes. (a) The kinetosomes of kinety *a* of *Gymnodinioides* (tomont) dividing in order to form kinety *b*. (b) The kinetosomes of kinety 1 of *Foettingeria* (tomont) producing kinety *a*. (c) Kineties of *Gymnodinioides* (tomite), showing the kinetosomes (*c.*) at the left (right of the observer) of the kinetodesma (*cd.*). Each kinetosome has a large satellite corpuscle and is connected by a desmose to a daughter kinetosome (*tc.*) which is a trichocystosome. (d) Kinety of *Polyspira* (protomont), showing the formation of trichocysts (*t.*) from the trichocystosomes (*tc.*). (e) Last division of *Foettingeria*. Formation of the kinetosomes of the future kineties *b* and *c* by the kinetosome of kinety *a*.

called a blepharoplast or kinetosome. In some cases, this kinetosome participates in the nuclear division, but this participation is often unnecessary. In many cases, the nucleus and kinetosome divide independently.

It is generally stated that the centriole of animal cells may give rise to flagella and behave like a blepharoplast or a kinetosome. According to E. Chatton (1924 and 1931), this proposal must be inverted. The centriole is phylogenetically and primarily the organelle giving rise to the flagellum. It may, in some cases, participate in nuclear division. Every centriole is a kinetosome, but every kinetosome is not a centriole.

The careful study of hundreds of flagellates has revealed that the kinetosome is always formed by the division of a pre-existing kinetosome. It is endowed with genetic continuity, and its existence has been demonstrated even in non-motile stages of the life cycle. This kinetosome gives rise to the flagellum. It is able to multiply independently of the nucleus, thus giving rise to chains of kinetosomes. The careful study of numerous ciliates has shown that the kinetosomes of ciliates are also endowed with genetic continuity. Even in forms which are devoid of cilia during a long period of their life cycle, the kinetosomes may often be seen organized, forming what we have called with E. Chatton and M. Lwoff (1929) an "infraciliature." And the kinetosomes of the ciliated "embryo" will be formed from these pre-existing kinetosomes. But kinetosomes are not only able to divide and to produce cilia. They are able to secrete fibers, to give rise to other granules producing trichocysts or trichites.

They play a prominent role in development, differentiation, and morphogenesis of ciliates. They move and vary constantly.

These cytoplasmic organelles, endowed with genetic continuity, live in a genetically constant system, thus providing a beautiful model of a self-reproducing particle whose activity is controlled by its environment [*cf.* A. Lwoff (1949b)].

My intention is to study the behavior of kinetosomes during the life cycle of some ciliates, to analyze and to discuss the various aspects of their movements and activity in development, differentiation, division, and evolution.

The reader will be perhaps badly shocked by some repetitions. But it was not possible to describe morphological phenomena without a single mention of the problems raised, and it was also felt that the theoretical implication of each set of data should be considered separately. Repetitions are the inevitable consequence of this procedure, the counterpart of which should be clarity.

CHAPTER 2

# The Complicated Life Cycle of *Gymnodinioides inkystans*

We are now in a position to consider some apostomatous ciliates.* This is a very homogeneous group, primarily associated with Crustacea. Many of these ciliates have two hosts. All have very remarkable and unique properties. They show a complicated life cycle, each phase of which is characterized by a peculiar structure that is the consequence of important movements of the ciliary system. On the gills of the hermit crab, *Eupagurus bernhardus,* are numerous cysts of the ciliate *Gymnodinioides inkystans.* This is the phoretic phase or phoront. Excystation occurs only at the molt of the host, and the small ciliate penetrates the discarded exoskeleton. This is the trophic stage or trophont. In 6 to 10 hours the ciliate has increased its volume up to 32 times. The trophont then escapes from the exoskeleton and after some hours encysts and divides. Let us call this stage tomont. The small ciliates or tomites thus formed escape from the cyst and swim actively. They may enjoy a free life for 6 to 8 days. If they find a crab, they encyst on the teguments; if not, they die.

The trophic phase corresponds to the ingestion and concentration by the ciliate of the violet astacin-protein of the crab. During this phase, the cytoplasm of the trophont is

* All the data on these ciliates are taken from E. Chatton and A. Lwoff's extensive monograph (1935). A good summary of this work has been given by H. B. Kirby in Calkins and Summer's book, *Protozoa in Biological Research.*

reduced to a thin peripheral layer containing the macro- and the micronucleus. When the fully grown ciliate leaves the molted exoskeleton, expansions of the cytoplasm divide the accumulated food.

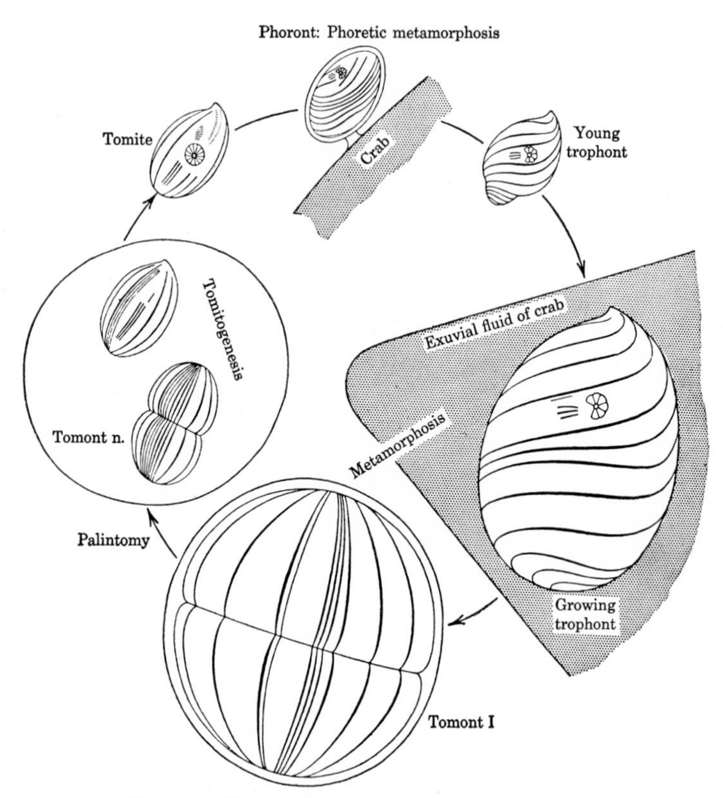


FIG. 2. *Gymnodinioides inkystans:* life cycle.

The single enormous ingested lump is then reduced to ellipsoidal platelets. These reserves are consumed during the phoretic phase, which may last some months, until the ecdysis of the host takes place. When the reserves are digested, they first turn pink, owing to the separation of the astacin from the protein, and finally astacin is precipitated as small red granules. It is worth mentioning that reserves may remain undigested for weeks or even months, thus providing a unique example of the persistence of a protein in a foreign protoplasm.

What is the intimate structure of these ciliates? The trophic phase, as it may be seen after silver impregnation, shows nine rows of cilia diverging from the anterior pole or its vicinity. Each of these rows has a given pattern, constant for the species. Four short rows are present in the equatorial sector of the ciliate. The rosette or mouth organ, not represented on the scheme, is located at the anterior end of the rows *x, y, z*. Each of the ciliary rows or kinety has a line of kinetosomes. At their right, the right of the ciliate (which corresponds to the left of the observer), is a fine thread which underlines the line of kinetosomes. In all ciliates, this kinetodesma is always at the right of the kinetosomes. This is the law of desmodexy [E. Chatton, A. Lwoff (1935b)]. The kinetodesma is probably an asymmetrical structure. Its relation to the kinetosomes is not yet clear.

After encystment, the ciliate undergoes a detorsion accompanied by an elongation of the rows *a, x, y, z,* which is essentially due to rapid divisions of the kinetosomes.

But, whereas in the rows *x, y, z* the kinetosomes remain in line, the kinetosomes of *a* divide towards their left. These granules become lined in a new row *b*.

It is clear enough that the course and the length of the rows depend on the phase of the life cycle.

It is clear also that the division of kinetosomes is induced by some changes in the underlying cytoplasm. The simplest hypothesis is, for the time being, that growth of the kinetosomes and their subsequent division depend on the presence of some specific foodstuffs. We may consider also the hypothesis that, when kinetosomes are too numerous to be lined in one row, they invade the adjacent space where they form new lines. All these interpretations will be considered later on.

Once the detorsion is achieved, the ciliate has a bipolar set of nine rows plus the rows *a*, *b* and *x*, *y*, *z*. It will now undergo a series of repeated divisions: this is palintomy.

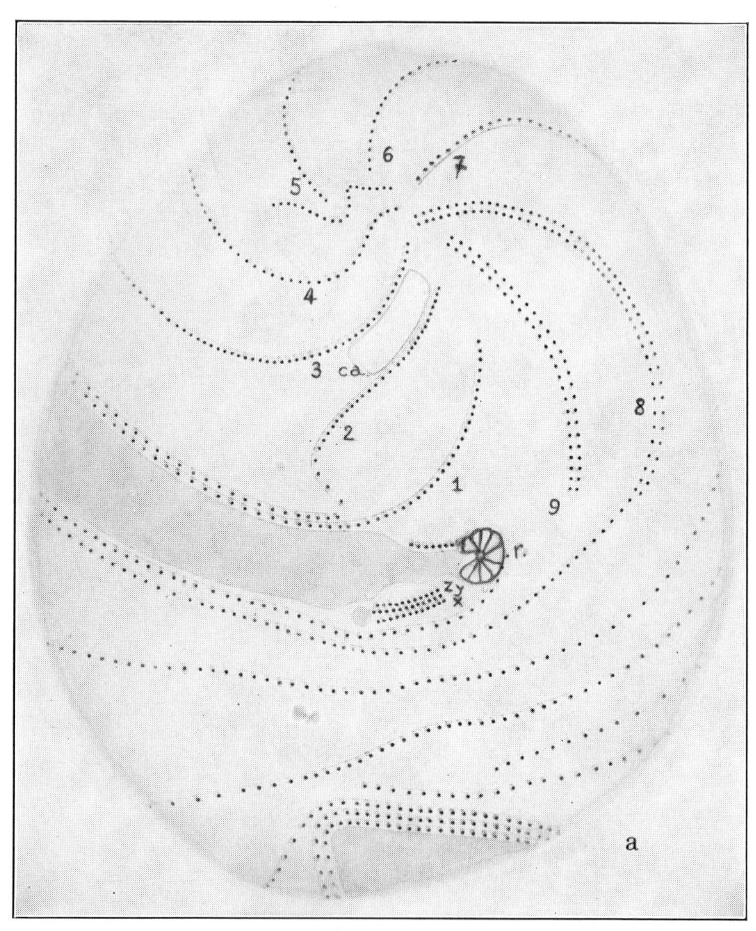


FIG. 3. *Gymnodinioides inkystans.* (a) The trophont. (b) The tomite (p. 13). The trophont's volume may be 2 to 64 times that of the tomite. *c.a.*, "cadre anastomotique": a characteristic fiber of many apostomatous ciliates, always located between kineties 2 and 3; *r.*, rosette or mouth organ; *ch.f.*, falciform field (thigmotactic); *ch.og.*, ogival field (also thigmotactic); *g.i.*, infraciliary granule (kinetosome); *tc.*, trichocystosome; *t.*, trichocyst.

During these divisions, all the rows remain bipolar, except the system *x*, *y*, *z*. The anterior and posterior parts of this system disappear before each division, and only three short segments remain in the equatorial part. The kinetodesma,

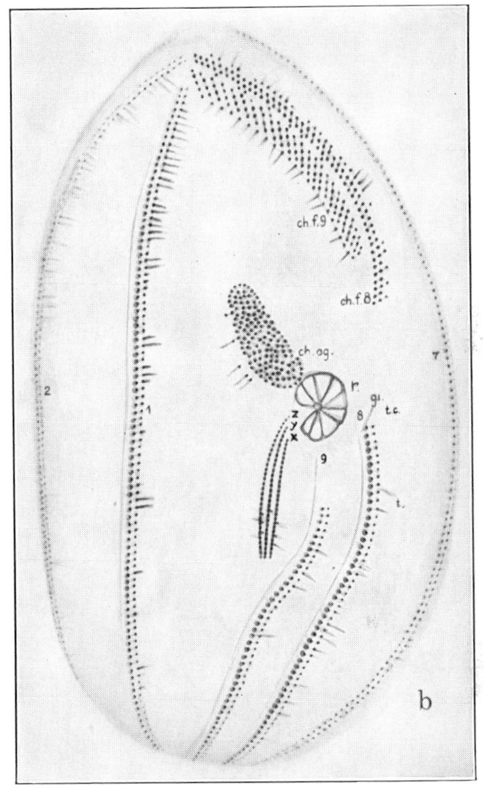


FIG. 3b. See legend for Fig. 3, p. 12.

as well as the kinetosomes, disappears, as if the maintenance of the kinetosome, as well as its growth and division, depended on the properties of the underlying cytoplasm. As we shall see, this conclusion will be reached frequently.

Divisions continue. One more ciliary row, *c*, has been formed. The division stops when the size of the tomites is reached. This happens after one to five divisions, according

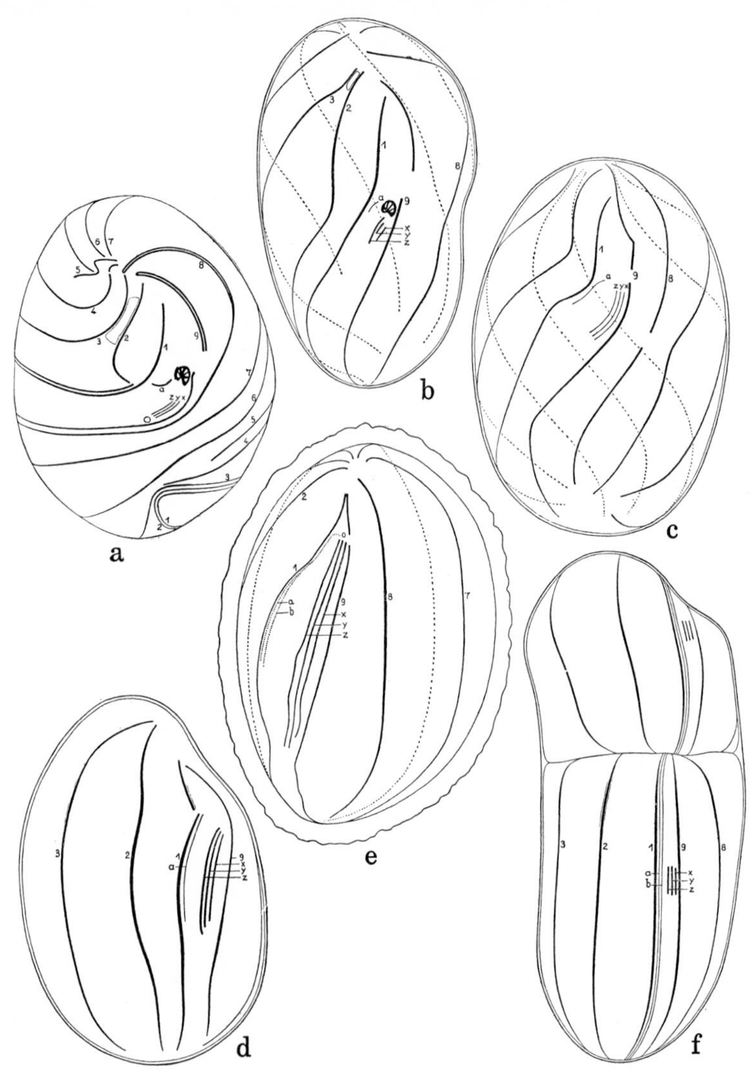


Fig. 4. *Gymnodinioides inkystans.* (a) Trophont. (b), (c), (d), (e) Protomonts. (f) Tomont. Note the detorsion of the ciliature, the elongation of kineties *a, x, y, z;* in the tomont (f), reduction of *x, y, z* in the interval of two divisions.

to the importance of growth at the trophic phase, thus yielding two to thirty-two tomites.

Important changes take place during this last period.

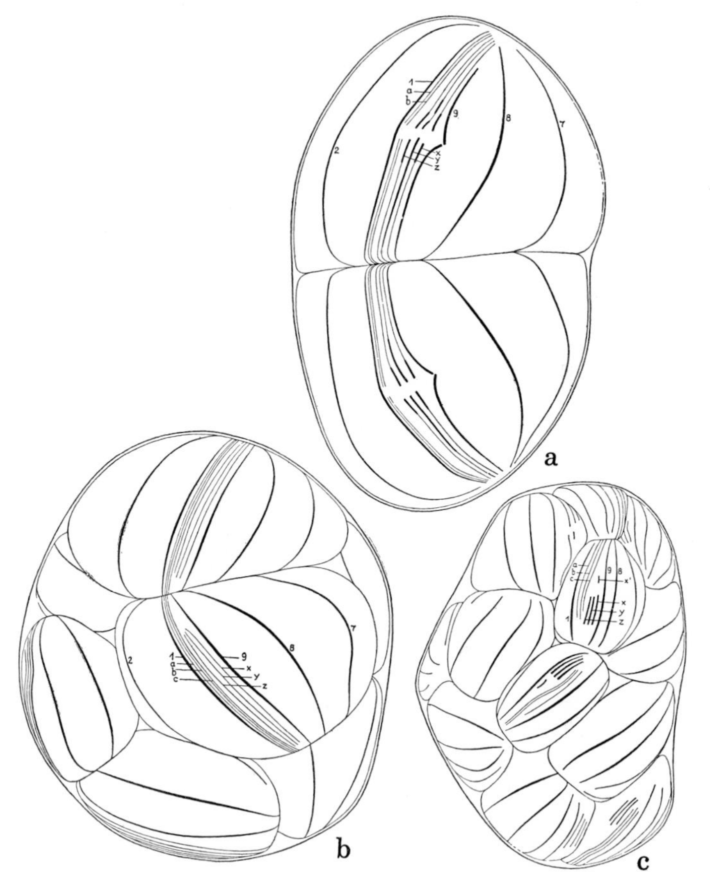


Fig. 5. *Gymnodinioides inkystans:* palintomy. (a) Two tomonts. (b) Eight tomonts. (c) Sixteen protomites.

The rows $x$, $y$, $z$ are progressively reduced in size. However, an anterior segment of $x$ has been detached which will give rise to the primordium of the rosette or mouth organ. A part of the rows $b$ and $c$ gradually becomes condensed in a small field of granules, which disappear. The row *a* gives rise to another ellipsoidal field.

While these processes are on the way, the middle part of the rows 8 and 9, kinetodesma and kinetosomes, disappears. The kinetosomes of the anterior part undergo one division. But the tomite is not yet ripe. In order to be ripe, the two granules of the row 9 have to divide once more, thus giving four rows of granules.

During the early period of tomitogenesis cilia have appeared. They are not represented on the drawings. They are ordinary cilia, all over the body. However, the rows 8 and 9 and the field *a* produce specialized thigmotactic cilia which have the property of ceasing their movements when coming into contact with a solid surface, thus assuring adherence to the substrate. This important patch of specialized cilia will allow the tomite to attach itself and to encyst on the integument of the crab.

Let us now imagine a morphologist looking at the living tomite and considering these specialized cilia without knowing their origin. His conclusion would be that the formation of this specialized structure is the result of the action of an organizer.

Dalcq and Pasteels, explaining the neural induction, postulate a multiplication of particles in the neural system under the influence of an organizer, and compare these granules with a virus. An agent possessing the ability to induce multiplication of such granules would be, according to Dalcq and to Brachet, an "evocator." This conception applies very well to the formation of the thigmotactic field, with the difference that we see the granules really multiplying. There is of course no reason to refer to self-reproducing cytoplasmic units as viruses.

Before escaping the cyst, the tomite has to form trichocysts, but this phenomenon will be examined later on.

When analyzing development, embryologists have found that the original control of differentiation in all cases appears to be exerted in relation to what may be called a morphogenetic field.

According to J. Huxley and G. de Beer (1934), "The

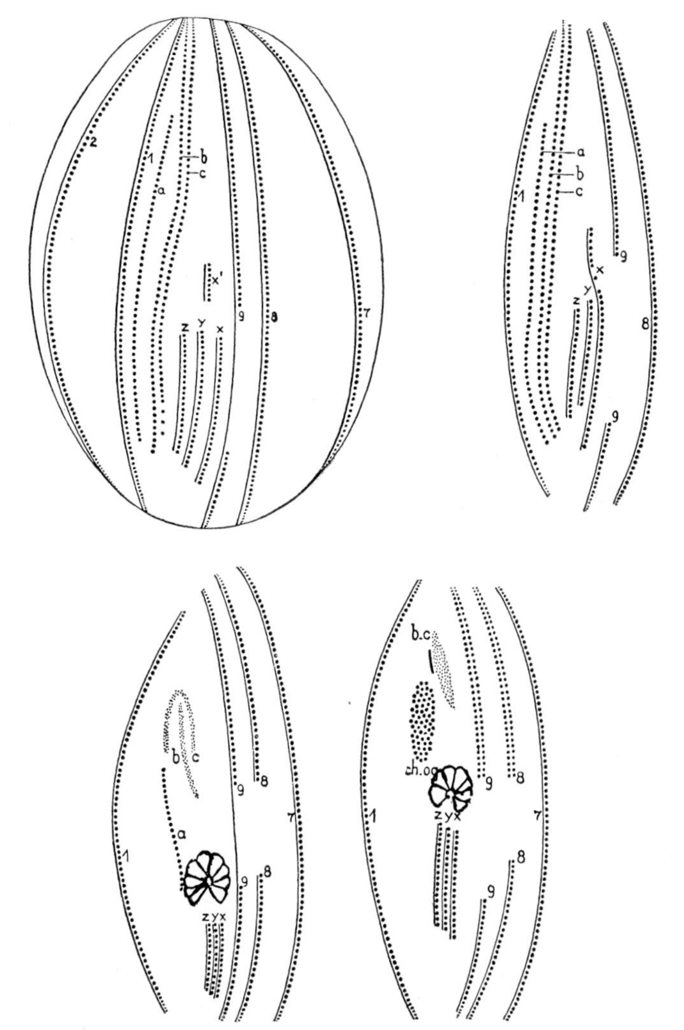


Fig. 6. *Gymnodinioides inkystans:* tomitogenesis. Formation of the ogival field (*ch.og.*) from $a$. Migration of $b + c$. Disappearance of the median part of 8 and 9. Isolation of a sector of $x$, $x'$ which is going to form the rosette (see the complete tomite on Fig. 3b).

term *field* implies a region throughout which some agency is at work in a coordinated way, resulting in the establishment of an equilibrium within the area of the field." "A field," says Waddington, "is a system of order such that the position taken up by unstable entities in one portion of the system bears a definite relation to the position taken up by the unstable entities in other portions."

The region between the rows 7 and 1 corresponds to such a field. The kinetosomes behave differently according to their position. Their maintenance, or their growth and division, depend evidently on the properties of the underlying cytoplasm.

The simplest hypothesis, for the time being, is that kinetosomes must get some specific food in order to grow and divide, and that the specific food must be unequally distributed in the region between the rows 7 and 1. In terms of molecular ecology one should question also the possible role of some specific cytoplasmic particles which could be directly or indirectly responsible for the nursing of kinetosomes.

CHAPTER 3

# How the Disarmed Tomite Proceeds to Manufacture Explosive Weapons in the Form of Trichocysts

We have considered only what we may call "normal" kinetosomes, able to produce cilia. But kinetosomes may acquire new properties.

Until the end of tomitogenesis, the structure of the ciliary row is simple. The kinetodesma is at its right. At the left, we see the kinetosomes with the cilia and another corpuscle, sometimes called the "kinetoplast," which is produced together with the cilia and represents perhaps only the enlarged basis of the cilium itself. But at the end of tomitogenesis, all the kinetosomes divide. The daughter granule is produced on the left in all the rows, except in the thigmotactic field of 9, where it is produced at the right.

These daughter granules do not produce cilia. They form a cylindrical rod which elongates towards the inside of the ciliate. These organelles are capable of being extruded under the influence of certain stimuli; they are trichocysts.

The formation of trichocysts has, for a very long time, been obscure. All possible origins have been assigned to them: nucleus, vacuoles, mitochondria, superficial network; all except the right one. This confusion was due to the fact that trichocysts are generally formed at any moment. In *Gymnodinioides,* they are formed at only one phase of the life cycle [E. Chatton, A. and M. Lwoff (1931b)]. The picture is very clear, and it is perhaps necessary to state that its diagrammatic representation corresponds to what is really seen under the microscope. It is obvious that each trichocyst is generated by one granule and that this granule results from the division of a kinetosome. Here, we are faced with an important phenomenon. The kinetosome has not only the properties of growth, division, and the production of cilia. It has also other possibilities or, as embryolo-

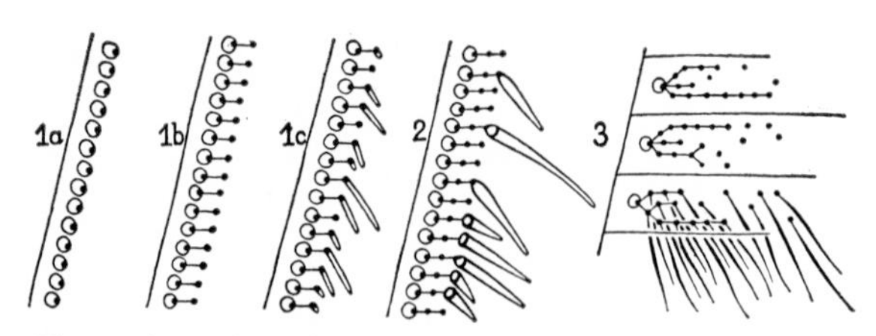


Fig. 7. Formation of trichocysts and trichites. (1) *Gymnodinioides:* (a) The normal ciliary row. Kinetosomes *c* and satellite corpuscles *s*. The kinetodesma is at the right of the kinetosomes (desmodexy). (b) Division of the kinetosomes; trichocystosomes are produced. (c) Formation of trichocysts in *Gymnodinioides*. (2) Formation of trichocysts in *Polyspira*. (3) Formation of trichites in *Foettingeria*.

gists would say, prospective potencies. A cilium-bearing kinetosome may, under certain circumstances, divide and give rise to a new granule which will not produce cilia but trichocysts. A granule never produces a cilium and a trichocyst. It produces either a cilium or a trichocyst.

We have reached the conclusion that kinetosomes may divide and produce cilia. We see that the ultimate phase of tomitogenesis reveals a new potency of the kinetosome.

Let us now recall the conclusions arising from the study of *Gymnodinioides*. Growth, division of the kinetosomes, production of cilia, production of trichocysts depend on the position of the granules on the ciliate and on the phase of the life cycle. And it is perfectly clear that the "position" or the "phase" is not a metaphysical property. It is obvious that growth, division, and metabolism of kinetosomes, as revealed by the production of cilia or trichocysts, depend on the properties of their environment.

The study of other forms of apostomatous ciliates will reinforce these conclusions and provide more data about kinetosomes.

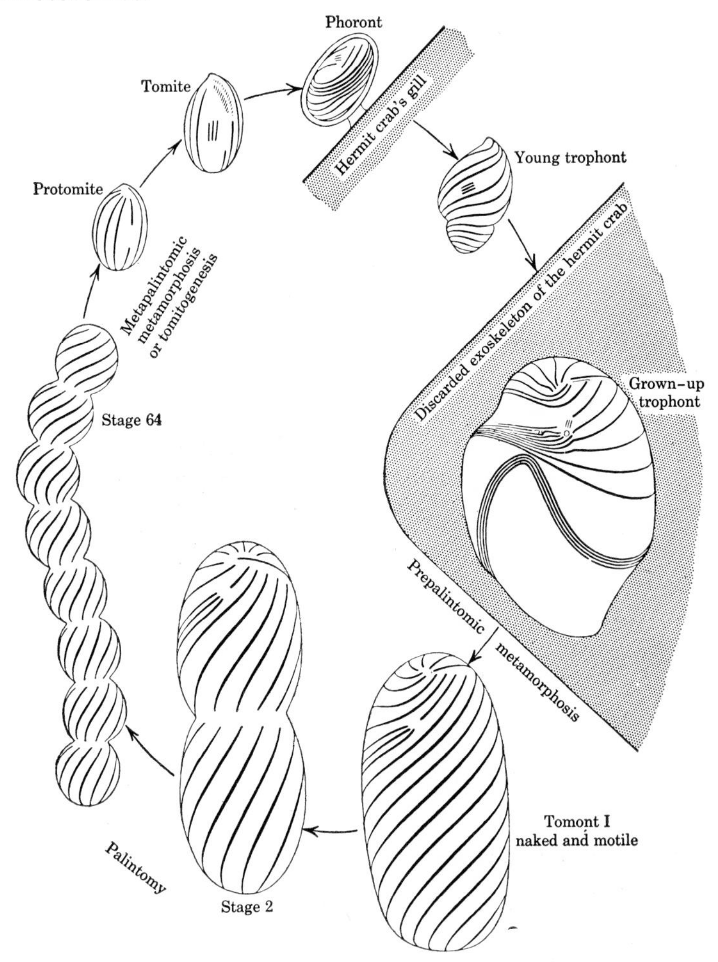


Fig. 8. *Polyspira delagei:* life cycle.

*Polyspira delagei* lives as a phoront together with *Gymnodinioides* on the skin of hermit crab; it grows in the exoskeleton and behaves like *Gymnodinioides* (Fig. 8). But there is no encystment of the grown-up trophont, which divides when motile and produces numerous long chains of tomonts.

The tomont at the last division is shown in Fig. 9a. Between the ciliary rows, some trichocysts are seen, the origin of which will be considered later. Between the rows 1 and 9, we recognize the rows *x, y, z* and an anarchic field of granules. The latter has been generated by the multiplication of granules of the row *a,* and will be organized in three rows during the early stage of the formation of tomite. The rows *b* and *c* will migrate towards the anterior end and eventually degenerate. The granules of *a* will multiply again and form one of the thigmotactic fields.

During all this period, the ciliate is motile; cilia are to be seen everywhere except on the rows *a, b, c.*

It thus appears that, whereas the majority of kinetosomes all over the ciliate produce cilia, the kinetosomes of certain regions are devoid of their characteristic production: cilia. The problems raised by this situation will be discussed in the next chapter.

Later on, the granules of *b* and *c* disappear; the granules of *a* produce persistent cilia. Here again, it is obvious that the fate of the granules depends on the properties of the underlying cytoplasm. This conclusion is reinforced by the consideration of some abnormal cases in which the granules of *b* and *c* also produce cilia.

The mature tomite also shows this beautiful production of trichocysts. It is again perfectly clear that the trichocyst arises from a granule which has been formed by division of a kinetosome. During the growth of the trichocyst, the granule takes the form of a ring, as centrosomes often do, e.g., in spermiogenesis. The ring seems to become a part of the trichocyst itself. The granule having produced a trichocyst seems unable to produce new granules, that is to say, to divide.

But in *Polyspira,* the production of trichocysts is not limited to the tomite. It starts before the first division. At

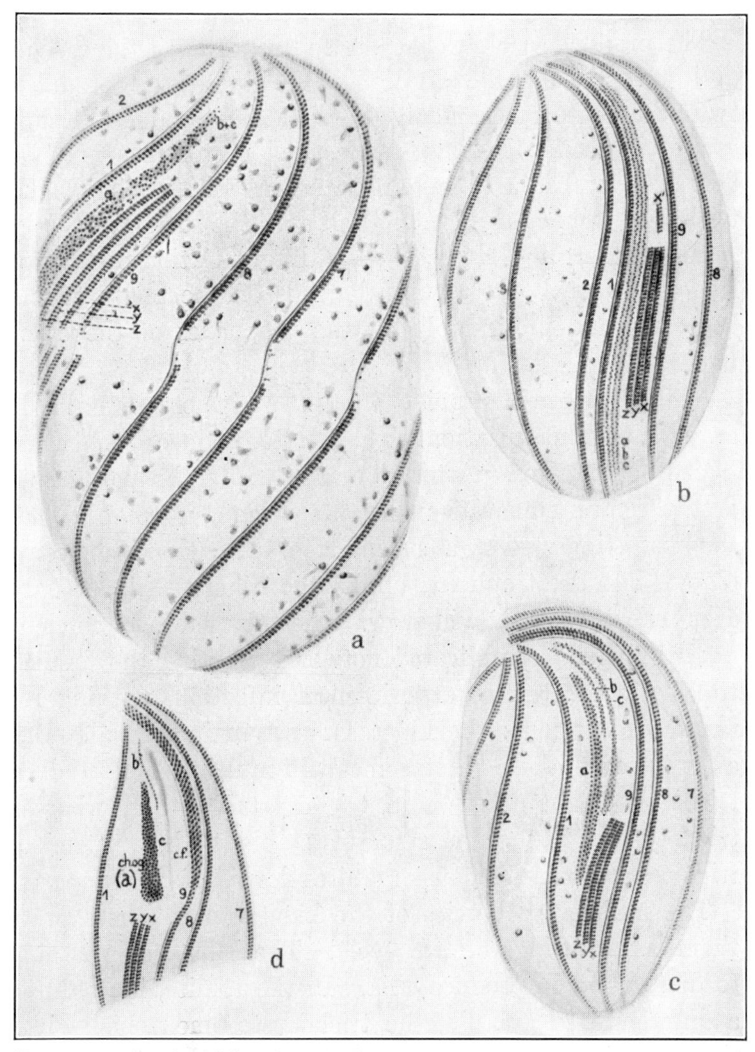


FIG. 9. *Polyspira delagei.* (a) Last division. (b), (c), (d) Tomitogenesis. Formation of the ogival field (*ch.og.*) from *a*. Disappearance of *b* and *c*. *c.f.*, "falciform," thigmotactic, field.

this phase, the production of trichocystosomes proceeds in exactly the same way as in the tomite.

The production of trichocysts continues until the second division. During the divisions, the kinetosome produces two trichocystosomes. Only the distal one produces trichocysts. It seems that also some trichocystosomes may be detached, are able to migrate, and are the origin of the trichocysts which are scattered all over the surface.

Here again, it is clear that the differentiation of kinetosomes into trichocystosomes depends on the phase of the life cycle and presumably on the properties of the cytoplasm.

*Foettingeria* will provide another and more remarkable example of differentiation. The tomite produces trichocysts like other tomites. After liberation from the palintomic cyst, the tomite encysts on a non-specific crustacean. When the host is ingested by a coelenterate, the cycle will be completed, but the trophont, unlike the others, will not only accumulate food. It will grow. The enlarged macronucleus finally forms a complicated network. During the first 12 to 14 days, after an experimental infection, nothing remarkable happens: the kinetosomes remain normal. But after 2 weeks, these kinetosomes will multiply and produce trichites. These differ from trichocysts in that, whereas trichocysts are tubular structures able to be protruded, trichites are homogeneous organites devoid of this property.

The multiple potencies of the kinetosomes thus express themselves during the life cycle. The kinetosome is able to divide and to produce cilia. In the tomite, it produces a differentiated granule, the trichocystosome, which gives rise to a trichocyst. In the 2-week-old trophont it produces differentiated granules, the trichitosomes, which multiply and produce trichites. The fate of the granule is controlled not only by its position, but also by the phase of the life cycle.

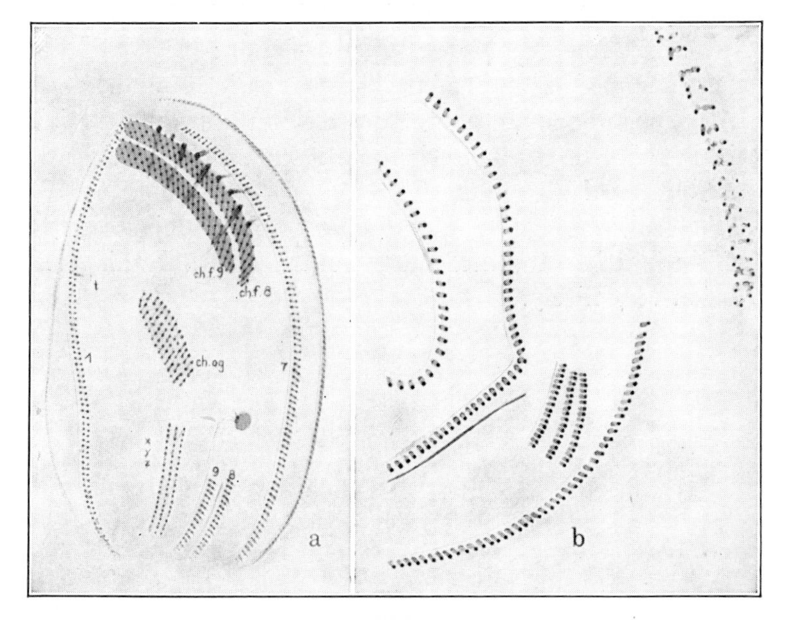


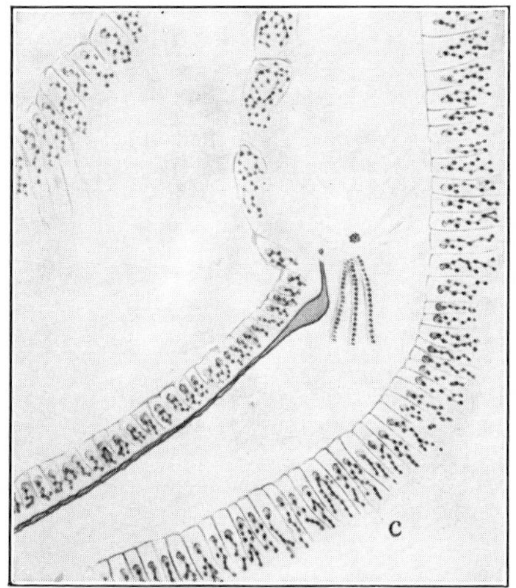


Fig. 10. *Foettingeria actiniarum.* (a) Tomite, showing the small trichocysts of the kinety 1 and the large trichocysts of the falciform fields 8 and 9. (b) Young trophont (less than 14 days); no trichocysts or trichites. (c) Old trophont (more than 16 days), showing the trichitosomes.

May I quote here an opinion of Sewall Wright (1941), discussing some problems of differentiation: "The stability of the changed state certainly becomes easier to understand if it is postulated that there are self-duplicating materials within the cell which can become modified chemically and multiply as of the new sort."

The self-duplicating kinetosomes, able to give rise to self-duplicating trichitosomes, would illustrate this conclusion very nicely.

CHAPTER 4

## Aspects of the Kinetosome

One kinetosome is always generated by division of another. We see kinetosomes dividing and have no evidence whatsoever of their formation *de novo*. They are endowed with genetic continuity. It is the custom to refer to such particles as "self-reproducing" or "autocatalytic" units. These terms should not be understood as implying that the particles are independent. A self-reproducing granule is by no means a self-sufficient granule. When we refer to kinetosomes as self-reproducing units, this means only that the kinetosome never arises *de novo,* and that some specific structure or template, present in the kinetosome, is necessary to organize other molecules into a new kinetosome: like genes, they can only be generated by, or in the presence of, an equivalent structure

The maintenance of these kinetosomes depends on local conditions. This is clear when we consider the rows $x, y, z$. These rows, bipolar in the tomont, are reduced in the trophont to short segments with a small number of kinetosomes. One can interpret this in two ways: either the postulated specific substance necessary for the maintenance of the kinetosome is present in limited amounts and disappears in certain regions of the ciliate; or, in these region a new substance, or enzyme, is formed, which dissolves or lyses the kinetosomes. The choice between these two possibilities is difficult.

Let us remember here one of tne propositions of Paul Weiss (1947) concerning molecular ecology: "Survival and orderly function of the total population are predicated on the presence of all essential members in definite concentrations, combinations, and distributions."

It is clear also that kinetosomes need some food not only to live but also to grow and to multiply, and probably some specific food. It has been noted that, at certain phases of the life cycle, kinetosomes of one region multiply whereas others do not. The specific food must therefore be concentrated in certain areas. We may quote here another of Weiss's conclusions: "If the specific existential and operational prerequisites for the various molecular species and groups differ at different sites of the cell, different species will automatically become segregated into their appropriate ecological environments. As a result, even a wholly indiscriminate mixture can become sorted out into a definite space pattern."

It seems plausible to admit that localization of specific molecules is controlled by their affinities for some differentiated parts of the cortex or, in the last analysis, by the properties of the given molecule and of the cortex. The hypothesis cannot of course be excluded that these specific substances are formed only in some areas owing to the distribution of some specific enzymes.

The granules of anarchic fields may become oriented in longitudinal rows. They are evidently submitted to some mysterious and powerful field of forces.

Proposition 6 of Paul Weiss (1947) fits very well with this hypothesis: "Organization in space of the content of the cell, and of any of its constituent particulate elements as well, therefore, presupposes a primordial system of spatially organized 'conditions' to set the frame for the later differential settlement of different members of the dispersed molecular populations."

When we look upon the whole series of changes which take place throughout the life cycle between the rows 7 and

1, we are prepared to admit A. L. Cohen's conclusion (1942) regarding the organization of protoplasm: "We must realize that a surface on the microscale is not a mathematical plane, but a layer of more or less oriented molecules or atoms with fields of forces which in some instances may be quite powerful."

Now it is obvious that, in *Gymnodinioides,* there are variations of properties from the anterior to the posterior pole, and from one meridian to another. The notion of morphogenetic field takes its full value and expresses itself in a spectacular way. Sinnott's (1939) definition of the morphogenetic field is here adequate because it is very general: "A field is the sum of the reactions which an entire protoplasmic system makes with its external and internal environment, reactions which are determined by the specific physiological activities of the living material of which the organism is composed."

It is obvious that the life history of kinetosomes is determined by specific changes of the environment. And this is true not only if we consider the maintenance and multiplication of kinetosomes, but also their specific metabolism.

The main and most characteristic product of the metabolism of kinetosomes is the cilium. Generally, all the kinetosomes of a ciliate are cilia-bearing kinetosomes. But many ciliates, either holotrichous ciliates like the *Sphenophryidae, Sphenophrya, Pelecyophrya,* or *Gargarius,* or suctorians, are devoid of cilia. Cilia appear only in the "embryo." This question will be examined later on. All that is necessary to know at this point is that the embryo loses its cilia, but that the kinetosomes persist. It is therefore obvious from these examples that the maintenance of a cilium, like its synthesis by the kinetosome, is controlled by the environment.

In *Gymnodinioides,* the kinetosomes of the fields *a, b, c,* while actively dividing, are devoid of cilia. This absence could be a question of environment. But there is of course a possibility that for kinetosomes, as for cells of higher organisms, there is an antagonism between multiplication and other specific activities, that is to say, an antagonism between the synthesis of "kinetosomal substance" and synthesis of ciliary substance. It is nevertheless possible to consider as certain that formation of cilia depends on the presence of one or more specific substance or substances, and also that environment controls the maintenance of cilia as it controls their formation.

It has been shown that, at the end of tomitogenesis, all the cilia-bearing kinetosomes divide, and the daughter granule produces a trichocyst. Kinetosomes may thus divide unequally: one of the granules remaining a kinetosome, the other producing a trichocyst or a trichite. It seems that the trichocystosome itself becomes a part of the trichocyst. Nevertheless, once a trichocystosome has expressed its prospective potencies, that is to say, the formation of a trichocyst, it is no longer endowed with self-reproducibility.

But before forming a specific product, the modified granule, the trichocystosome of the predivision phase of *Polyspira,* or the trichitosome of the trophont of *Foettingeria,* may undergo one or more divisions. The trichocystosome or the trichitosome is therefore, in some cases, able to live and to multiply as such.

Sewall Wright (1941), discussing some aspects of the physiology of the gene, has reached the following conclusion: "Differences in local conditions may bring about a differential accumulation of metabolism products arising by the interaction of cytoplasm, nuclear products, and the environment, and eventually bring about the elaboration of new plasmagenes in the cytoplasm of some regions of the organism. . . . It may be concluded that while the proteins of cytoplasm are probably autonomous with respect to basic structure, metabolic processes are dependent on active substances, probably of relatively low molecular weight, emanating from the nucleus."

Is it possible to apply this conception to the kinetosome?

If we consider one ciliate at a given phase of its cycle, we see that the formation of all the trichocystosomes from kinetosomes takes place simultaneously. This change is therefore not the result of a random modification, but the result of the interaction of the kinetosome with some specific substance.

It is nevertheless a complicated process involving:

*a.* The production by the kinetosome of a modified granule.

*b.* The production of a trichocyst or a trichite.

As, in the tomite, all the daughter kinetosomes produce trichocysts at once, two hypotheses must be considered:

1. All the kinetosomes have undergone a normal equational division. But the environment being changed, the interaction of the daughter kinetosome with these "conditions" results in the formation of a trichocyst instead of a cilium. This would mean an induced modification of the specific activity of the granule. The data concerning adaptive enzymes, which have been so pertinently and carefully reviewed by J. Monod (1947), allow the hypothesis that one substance could inhibit some enzymes, thus modifying the nature of the end product of the activity of the kinetosome. It is possible also to consider the hypothesis that kinetosomes possess many enzymes and that, owing to the availability of diverse substrates, one or the other of these enzymes is able to function.

2. The kinetosome has undergone an unequational division. As all the daughter kinetosomes produce trichocystosomes, this cannot be the result of a random modification. It can only be the result of the interaction of the mother kinetosome with some specific substances, that is to say, an induced modification.

During the trophic phase of *Polyspira,* trichocystosomes are formed and produce trichocysts whereas "normal" kinetosomes continue to produce cilia. Of course, there are considerable differences between a normal kinetosome and a trichocystosome. The first is close to the kinetodesma and, so far as we know, connected to it by a fiber. The second is far away (relatively) from the kinetodesma and not directly connected with it. It is therefore possible either (*a*) that the substance controlling the production of cilia is located near the kinetodesma; or (*b*) that the attachment to the kinetodesma is responsible for some orientation of an unknown material and controls the formation of cilia. The choice is difficult between alternatives *a* and *b*. It is also difficult between hypotheses 1 and 2.

But the one conclusion remains: the metabolism of the kinetosome and of its daughter particles is controlled by the environment. Thus one "plasmagene" may possess many prospective potencies and turn out different organelles according to its position and to the phase of the life cycle.

The study of apostomatous ciliates has thus led to the morphological demonstration of self-reproducing cytoplasmic units. We are able to conclude not only that specific cytoplasmic particles should exist, but also that they do exist.

The study of their behavior during the life cycle of the ciliates furnishes an illustration of the conceptions schematized by Weiss under the name "molecular ecology," which thus receives the support of visible allies.

The question of the equivalence of all kinetosomes will be discussed in Chapter 6. Let us admit, for the time being, that all kinetosomes are essentially equivalent, but are organized in different systems and structures, according to their position in the ciliate and the phase of the life cycle. And as these differences are observed in a single ciliate, the hypothesis of a change in the genome being responsible for these phenomena is excluded. The fates of the kinetosomes are largely phenotypical expressions of changes in the properties of their environment.

Thus kinetosomes illustrate in a most spectacular way the notion of morphogenetic field and of organizers. From the study of the life cycle of ciliates, it may be concluded that kinetosomes as a whole play a fundamental role in their morphogenesis.

But ciliates are non-cellular organisms. Are kinetosomes of any use in understanding the problem of morphogenesis in "higher organisms"? It is possible to consider that cells which do not produce cilia are unable to produce the specific substance which enables the formation of cilia. But it is easy also to visualize kinetosomes being segregated, so that cells which possess kinetosomes will develop cilia, whereas cells devoid of kinetosomes will not.

It is possible furthermore to consider that, if a kinetosome is changed into a trichocystosome, the potentiality of the host-cell will be changed: it will produce trichocysts instead of producing cilia.

Thus, the kinetosome provides a model for one possible mechanism of cell differentiation in higher animals.

A multicellular organism has differentiated cells. A ciliate has differentiated parts. It seems therefore important to point out that self-reproducing particles may behave in different ways in different parts of a ciliate, just as viruses behave in different ways in different cells of an organism.

C. Darlington (1939) considers the plasmagenes as "a relic of the naked gene of a remote prechromosomian period, a relic which has been preserved in spite of its being a nuisance in heredity because it is a necessary cog in the machinery of development." Kinetosomes considered as plasmagenes or as visible specific cytoplasmic units endowed with genetic continuity are perhaps a nuisance. But, in providing a useful model for concepts concerning specific cytoplasmic units which we are compelled to postulate, they are a helpful nuisance.

It is extremely difficult to understand how, during the development of an organism, cells with an apparently constant genome may become differentiated. The concept of the unequal distribution of specific units, or self-reproducing plasmagenes, has been built up to explain cell differentiation, and the concept of molecular ecology in order to explain cell and tissue organization. But we have no morphological or physiological data which would constitute a proof of the existence of any one of these postulated units. Also, it is really strange that biologists, faced with this problem, should have ignored or even denied the possible existence of cytoplasmic, visible, self-reproducing units.

Chatton and I, when working out the life cycle of apostomatous ciliates in the years 1923–1932, did not realize completely the possible importance of the kinetosomes for some of the future problems of developmental physiology and of molecular ecology.

The study of apostomes shows that different morphological types, different structures or patterns, organelles of different physiological function may be formed from the very same material, the kinetosome. The condition for these changes is a heterogeneous cortex. The movements of the kinetosomes are controlled by the metabolism.

A gene mutation modifying the enzymatic system would be able to produce hereditary morphological changes. But it must not be forgotten that kinetosomes represent a population of "self-reproducing" units. These units, like any other, must be able to undergo changes. If a change is favorable, the "mutated" kinetosome may replace the others. In many ciliates, kineties reproduce themselves by elongation; they are endowed with genetic continuity. It is therefore possible that different mutants of kinetosomes are selected in different meridians. Nevertheless, movements of kinetosomes are controlled by the metabolism. Metabolism is controlled by enzymes which are controlled by genes. Enzymatic activity is controlled by the presence of specific substrate. It thus appears that certain specific activities of an organism are under the triple control of genes, of self-reproducing cytoplasmic particles, and of the environment.

## CHAPTER 5

# Division, Absence of Division, Induced Division, and Morphogenesis

When considering the life cycles of apostomatous ciliates, one would be tempted to conclude that the arrangement of kinetosomes as it is seen in the structure of the tomite is the indirect consequence, or the necessary corollary, of modifications connected with, or controlled by, division. This hypothesis must now be considered in the light of some aberrant life cycles.

In any one of the species we have examined, it may happen that the trophont takes up only a small amount of food. These undernourished trophonts encyst. They do not divide. However, they undergo metamorphosis and give rise to a tomite. This tomite will encyst on its host.

Thus the complete series of metamorphosis, the movements of kinetodesma and kinetosomes, take place without division. They are obviously and necessarily the consequence of changes in the properties of the cytoplasm, which can only be the reflection of the metabolism as controlled by the interaction of hereditary outfit and external factors, including food.

The study of *Phoretophrya* will allow discussion of this obvious conclusion. The grown-up trophonts which escape the exoskeleton of *Nebalia* encyst and undergo detorsion. They may evolve in two different ways. They may follow the normal route: division, formation of a tomite, encystment. The phoront will escape at the molt. But a certain number of encysted ciliates, for some unknown reason, do not undergo division. They are transformed into one huge tomite. This tomite will escape the cyst, and after a short free life forms a new cyst on a *Nebalia*. This large phoront has lost the power to divide without an external stimulus. Division will start only some hours before the ecdysis of the host. It is apparently induced by some substance which

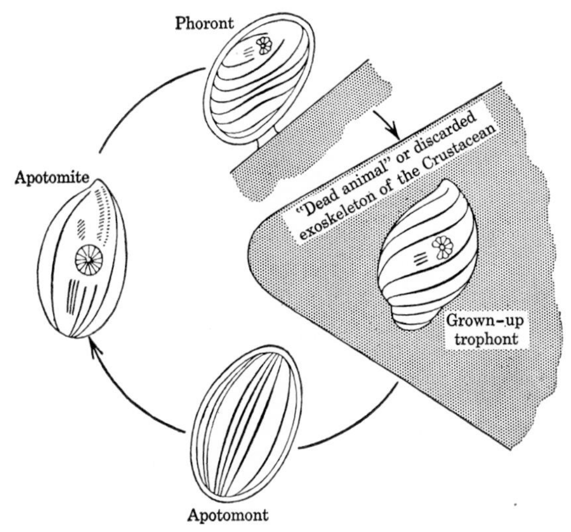


Fig. 11. Apotomy. The food intake by the trophont has been small. The cycle is completed without any division. Apotomy may occur in many species.

is excreted by the host at this period. Nevertheless, this induced division proceeds normally as in other species. However, after the last division, it is not the tomital structure which is produced, but the structure of the trophic phase.

When division takes place normally, the ciliate is organized into the tomital structure. When division takes place after a resting period and is induced by the ecdysis of the host, the ciliates have the structure of the trophont.

The situation is somewhat the same in *Synophrya hypertrophica*. The life cycle is represented on the diagram.

Just as those of *Gymnodinioides,* trophonts of *Synophrya* take up food in the discarded exoskeleton. They abandon the molt, encyst, and divide, and tomites are differentiated which encyst on the integument of the crabs. But the

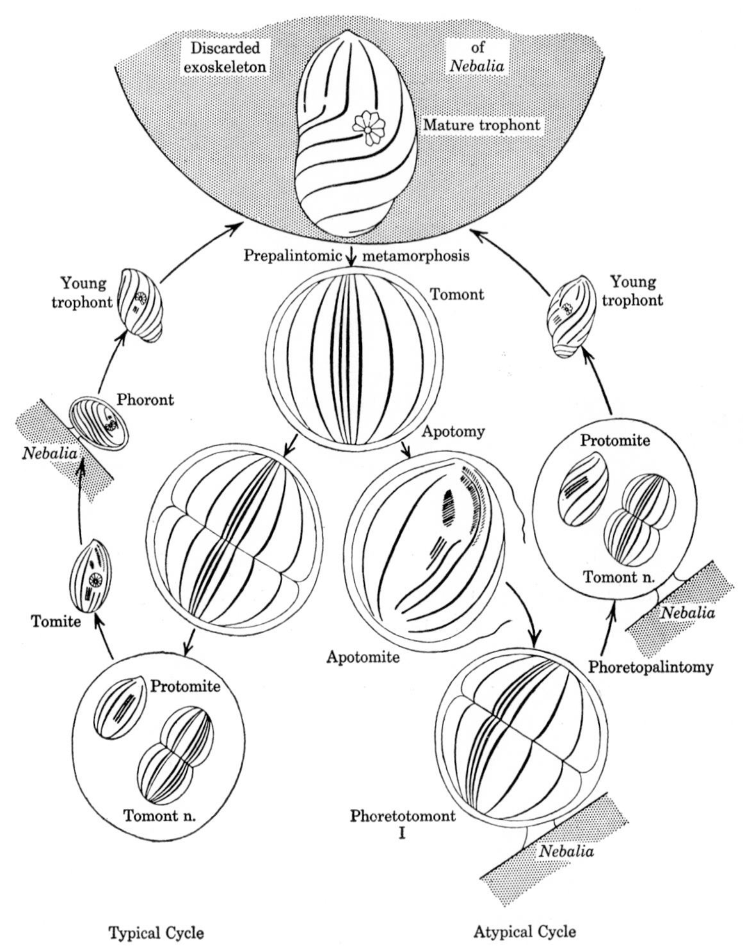


FIG. 12. *Phoretophrya nebaliae:* life cycle. Normal cycle on the left. On the right, formation of the huge apotomite which will encyst on a *Nebalia* and in which division is induced by the pre-ecdysic phenomena. The phoretotomite has a trophontal structure.

phoront, instead of awaiting ecdysis, inoculates itself in the crab. Leucocytes will form a barrier and isolate the parasite in a limited sector in which the ciliate feeds. The size

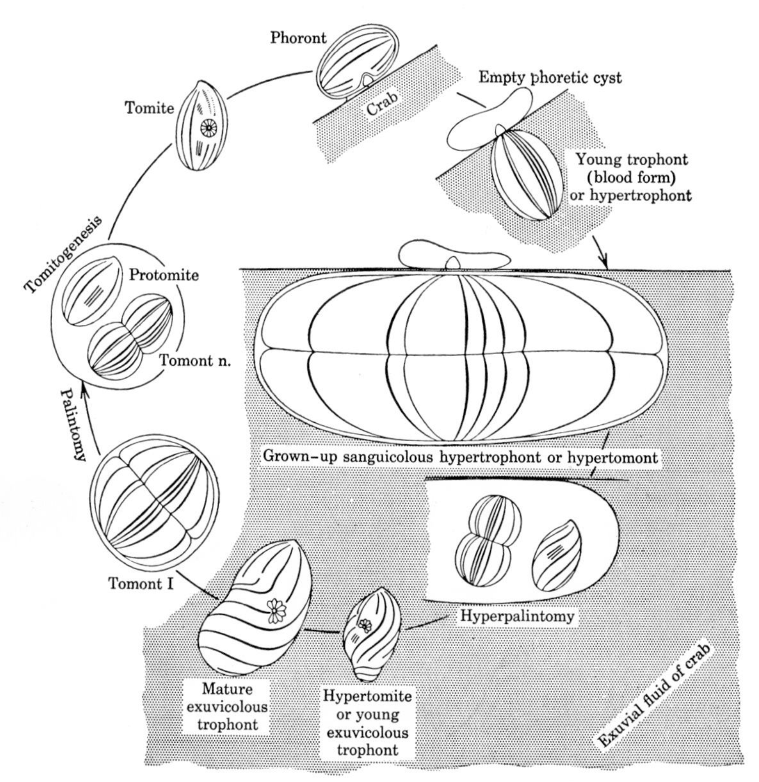


FIG. 13. *Synophrya hypertrophica:* life cycle. The division of the internal hypertrophont is induced by ecdysis. The hyperpalintomy yields trophonts.

increases enormously. The macronucleus is altered into a complicated network. The grown-up "hypertrophont" will now wait for ecdysis. The sexual behavior of the male crab allows us to see what happens before ecdysis takes place. It is known that copulation of crabs takes place only immediately after ecdysis of the female, between a hard male and a soft female. In order to copulate, the male has to select a female before ecdysis. A delicate pinching of the female limbs apparently enables him to recognize a change of consistency of the tissues 24 to 48 hours before the molt. He then climbs on the back of the female and

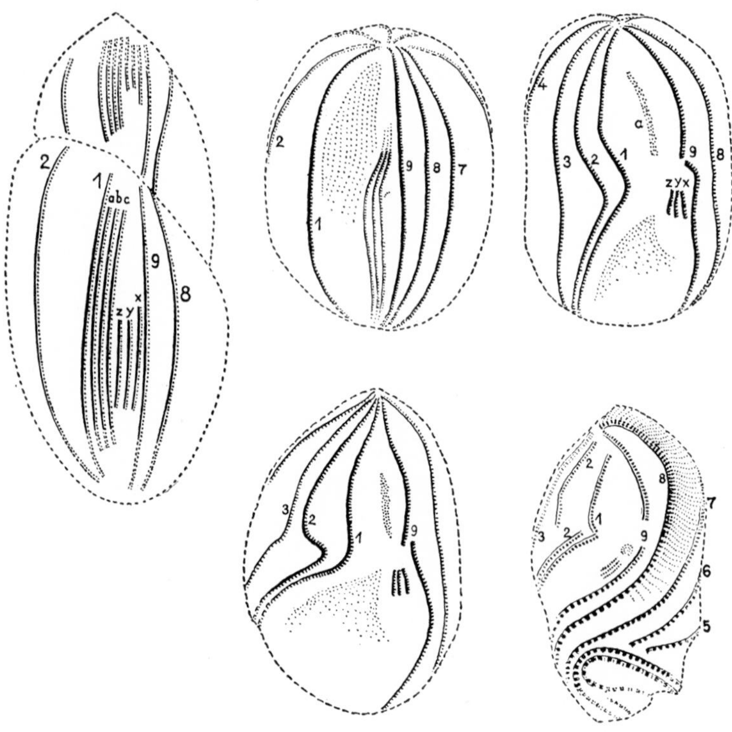


Fig. 14. *Synophrya hypertrophica.* Last division of the hypertomont and morphogenesis of the hypertomite with a trophontal structure.

waits. If such a male-carrying female is sacrificed, one finds that all the hypertrophonts are undergoing palintomy. Division is induced by some changes which take place 48 to 24 hours before ecdysis. However, this hyperpalintomy yields hundreds or thousands of ciliates with the typical structure of the trophont. They will escape after ecdysis, enter the molted exoskeleton, and behave as normal trophonts. Here, as in *Phoretophrya,* the ciliates formed after the ecdysis-induced palintomy are of the trophontal type.

Thus, *Synophrya* enjoys two palintomic phases: one takes place after growth in the molted exoskeleton and yields ciliates of the tomital structure. The other takes place after growth in the blood of the crab and a long resting phase and yields ciliates of the trophontal type. As far as visible superficial structures are concerned, palintomy and hyperpalintomy are identical. The difference lies in the postpalintomic phase. Obviously the phenomena which follow the last division are controlled by some metabolic process which is itself controlled by the metabolism of the trophont.

CHAPTER 6

# Genetic Continuity of Kineties and the Problems of Isolated Populations of Kinetosomes

The complicated series of events we have described poses two important problems: (1) Why do kinetosomes sometimes behave differently in different sectors of one kinety? (2) Why do different ciliary rows behave differently?

Let us consider first the rows 8 and 9. Their posterior part is simple like the other rows. The median part has disappeared, kinetodesma as well as kinetosomes. The kinetosomes of the anterior part have divided, once in the row 8 and twice in the row 9 (see Fig. 3b, p. 13).

It is perhaps necessary to point out that all kinetosomes of one kinety are equivalent. During division, the median kinetosomes become located either on the posterior part of the "proter" or on the anterior part of the "opisthe"; the proter is the anterior daughter ciliate, the opisthe the posterior one. It is therefore obvious that the fate of the kinetosomes of one kinety depends on its position on the ciliate. This means that the behavior of the kinetosomes, the facts that they remain without apparent change, that they disappear, that they multiply, depend on the properties of the underlying cytoplasm. The cytoplasm may be "neutral." It may produce the disappearance of the kinetosome or induce its multiplication. Properties of the cytoplasm vary in the anterior, median, and posterior parts of the kinety in the most conspicuous way.

If we consider the rows *x, y, z,* we reach the same conclusions. The conditions for their maintenance are realized only in the median part of the tomite.

The fact that the anterior sector of the kinety *x* will form the rosette or mouth organ seems to show that some special morphogenetical field is always located in the corresponding region. Nevertheless, the hypothesis cannot be excluded *a priori* that the kinetosomes and fibers of the row *x* possess some special properties which are responsible for their response. According to this hypothesis, the formation of the rosette would be not the effect of a localized morphogenetical field, but the reflection of the properties of a specialized kinety to conditions present everywhere. But it is difficult to understand, if this hypothesis is admitted, why it is not the kinety *x* as a whole which is turned into a rosette.

Nevertheless, this brings up the problem of the different behavior of different kineties. A somatic ciliary row of *Gymnodinioides* and of other apostomes is endowed with genetic continuity. A given somatic kinety of the proter and of the opisthe is the anterior or the posterior part of the parent's kinety. This is the type called "direct continuity by elongation" by E. Chatton and A. Lwoff. The reproduction of *x, y, z* is of the same type, with the difference that they are bipolar only before division, whereas in the resting phase they are reduced to a short segment of five to twenty kinetosomes, according to species.

In *Pericaryon cesticola y* and *z* have only two kinetosomes and *x* only one. What happens when the regression reaches its limit, that is to say, when a ciliary row present during one phase disappears during the following phase? How is it regenerated? In *Polyspira* and *Gymnodinioides,* the rows *b* and *c* disappear during the tomital and phoretic phase and are absent in the trophont. Before and during palintomy, the kinetosomes of *a* divide and form an anarchic field, the kinetosomes of which are later oriented in two lines *b* and *c*.

In *Foettingeria, a, b,* and *c* are formed anew from the kinetosomes produced by the kinety 1. In *Chromidina elegans* the whole "oral" system *a, b, c, x, y, z* is absent in the trophont. It is formed during palintomy from the kineto-

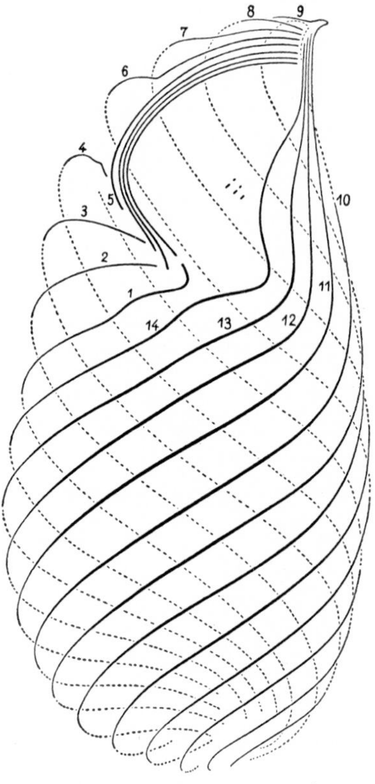


FIG. 15. *Pericaryon cesticola.* Kineties *y* and *z* are reduced to two kinetosomes; kinety *x* to one kinetosome.

somes derived from 1. This is a unique example among the ciliates of the formation *de novo* during one phase—tomite—of the oral ciliature absent during another phase—trophont. Some sort of regulation therefore exists.

These kinetosomes originating from one kinety behave differently from the mother kinetosomes which have remained in line in the mother kinety. Once again, we reach the conclusion that the fate of kinetosomes is controlled by the underlying cytoplasm. But this conclusion is not a contradiction of the fact that some kineties are endowed

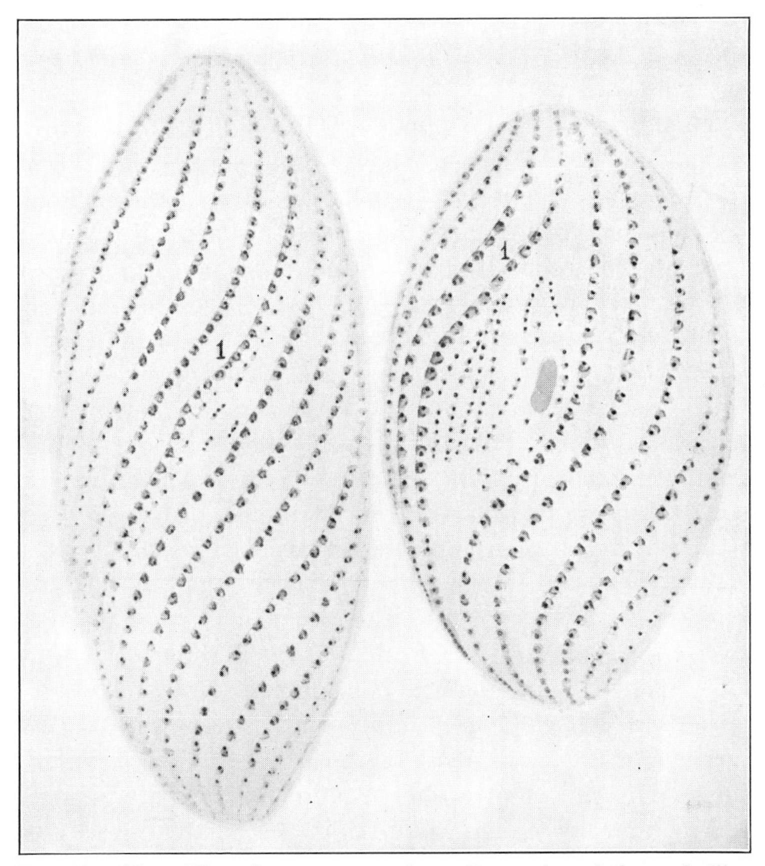


FIG. 16. *Chromidina elegans:* protomites. Formation of the oral ciliature by division of the kinetosome of kinety 1. The oral ciliature is totally absent in the trophont and in the tomont.

with genetical continuity by elongation. This means that more or less autonomous, self-perpetuating populations of kinetosomes formed by spontaneous mutations may be segregated in different meridians of the organism. And as conditions may be different in different meridians, there is a possibility that selection of mutated kinetosomes may take place. Thus the possibility that different lines of kinetosomes could be different cannot be excluded. A change in the morphology of a ciliate could be the result of a new response of populations of mutated kinetosomes to the same environment.

The work of T. Sonneborn and G. Beale (1949) has shown that under the influence of antisera the antigenic type of *Paramecium* is changed. An analysis of this phenomenon has brought the authors to the conclusion that the antigenic type was controlled by plasmagenes. Taking into account the paralyzing effect of antisera, I have been led (1949a) to the hypothesis that Sonneborn and Beale's antisera could act on cilia. The responsible antigens would be ciliary antigens. As cilia are produced by kinetosomes, these could have a share of responsibility in the Sonneborn-Beale phenomenon. The hypothesis according to which antiserum could orientate the selection of kinetosomes or modify their structure seems plausible. It is possible also that a substance analogous to the ciliary antigen could exist in the kinetosome. Nevertheless, the problem of relations between the ciliary material and the kinetosome's constituents endowed with genetical continuity is posed by Sonneborn and Beale's highly interesting experiments. This problem of the natural or experimental selection of kinetosomes remains one of the main problems of ciliate biology.

According to V. Tartar (1941), "the ciliates present us with a living fiber system having morphogenetic capacities." Are we really entitled to speak of "living fibers"? Or to consider that the visible cortical structure commands morphogenesis?

Tartar has cut *Paramecium* in such a way that the anterior part contained two nuclei but was devoid of oral structure. These pieces never regenerated the mouth; "a further evidence," writes Tartar, "of this rigid differentiation" in *Paramecium*. This may be true and could mean that some specialized kineties or kinetosomes are endowed with genetical continuity. This is plausible. We know that in the ciliate *Glaucoma scintillans* or *Leucophrys piriformis* (= *Glaucoma piriformis* = *Tetrahymena gelei*) the mouth is always produced by one kinety: the stomatogenic kinety or kinety 1 [E. Chatton, A. and M. Lwoff, J. Monod (1931)]. However, we do not know whether the property of the kinety 1 is related to the special properties of its kinetosomes or to the localization in its vicinity of specific "molecular species." Probably this asymmetry reflects the anisotropy of the cortex which is responsible for the action of these "molecular species" which we consider responsible for the reproduction of some localized kinetosomes and their organization into a specific pattern. But a mouthless *Paramecium* is unable to feed, and the hypothesis cannot be excluded that the absence of mouth formation is the result of starvation. The inability to regenerate the mouth could also be due to the removal of localized cytoplasmic organelles.

The problem of the autonomy and differentiation of kineties is not yet solved. Perhaps the heterotrichous ciliate *Licnophora* will provide a good example of its complexity. The ciliary system of *Licnophora chattoni* comprises two parts: the oral system and the basal system. According to the investigations of S. Villeneuve-Brachon (1940), the peristome of the daughter ciliate originates from one or a very few kinetosomes escaping from the original peristomial system of the mother. These kinetosomes multiply, thus forming an anarchic and homogeneous field of closely packed kinetosomes. Later on, kinetosomes are aligned and organized just as if submitted to some orienting forces. The kineties of the basal disc are reproduced by division (direct continuity by elongation).

W. Balamuth (1942) has performed some operations on another closely related species of *Licnophora, L. macfar-*

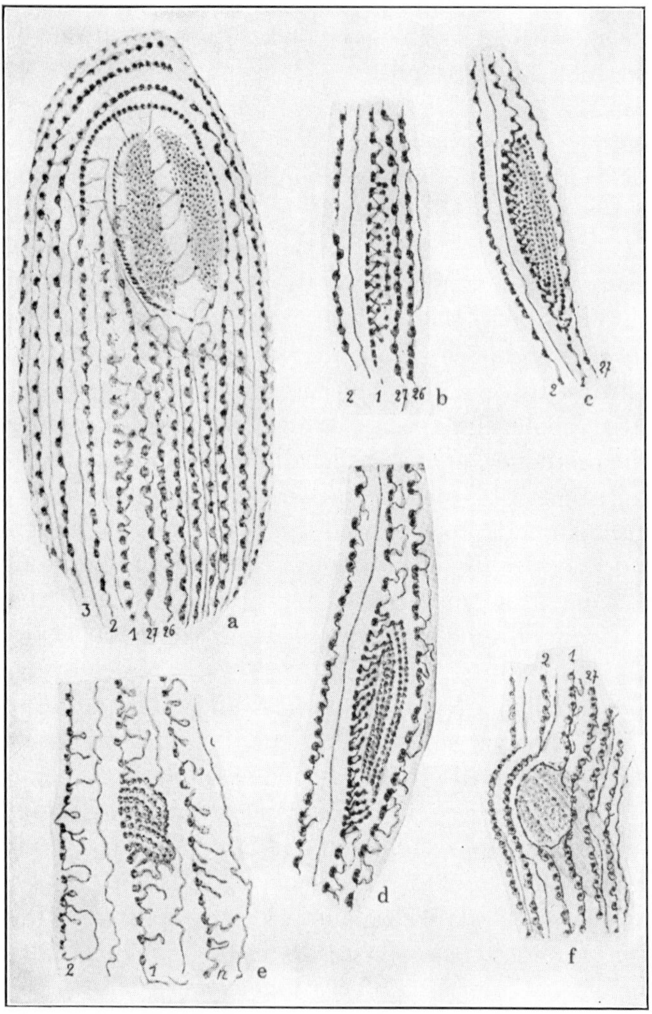


Fig. 17. Stomatogenesis in *Glaucoma scintillans* and *Leucophrys piriformis*. (a) *Glaucoma scintillans*. The very beginning of the mouth formation. Some kinetosomes have been produced at the left of the stomatogenic kinety 1. (b), (c), (d) Later stages of mouth formation. (e), (f) Stomatogenesis of *Leucophrys piriformis*. (e) Division of the kinetosomes of the stomatogenic row 1. (f) Mouth is completed.

*landi.* It appears that it is relatively easy for this ciliate to regenerate its peristomial zone, but it cannot regenerate the basal disc. This beautiful experiment unfortunately does

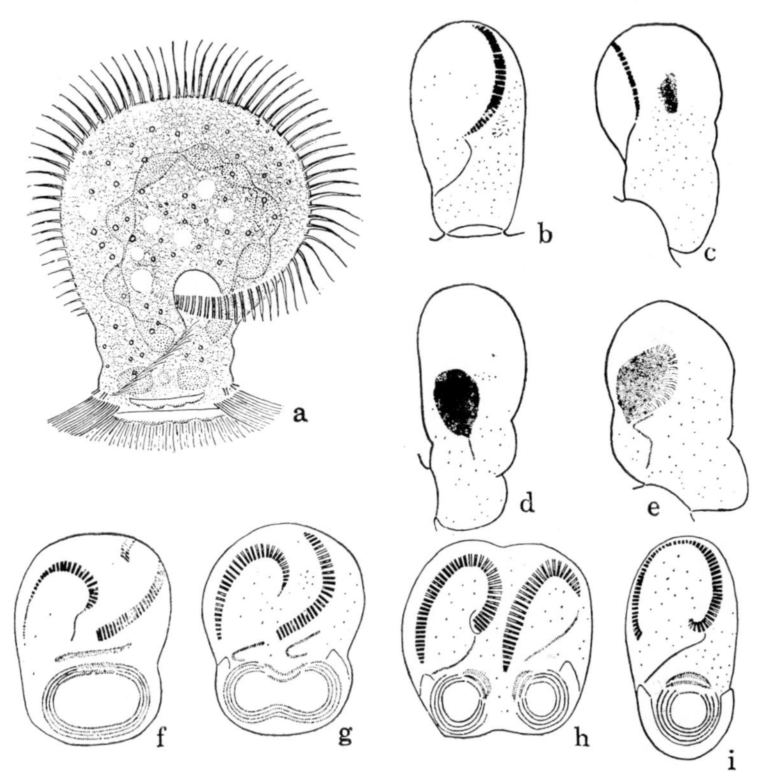


FIG. 18. *Licnophora chattoni.* (a) Ciliate *in vivo*. (b) Early stage of the stomatogenic field. (c), (d) The anarchic field. (e) Membranelles are modelled into the anarchic field. (f)–(i) Division of the ciliate, showing the reproduction of the basal disc.

not solve the problem. The inability to regenerate the basal disc with its ciliary system could be due: (*a*) to the suppression of a specialized line of kinetosomes; (*b*) to the suppression of some cortical elements endowed with genetical continuity; (*c*) to the suppression of both specialized kinetosomes and cortical organelles.

In apostomatous ciliates, the number of kineties remains constant throughout the cycle. But owing to the great differences of size, the distance between kineties varies enormously from the tomite to the mature trophont. In other parasitic ciliates, the phenomena are quite different. *Ichthyophthirius multifiliis* has been studied by H. Mugard (1947). The mature trophont has approximately 2040 kineties. This trophont encysts, undergoes palintomy, and gives rise to a great number—approximately 2800—of "theronts" or hunting forms. The theront has only 43 kineties. At the equator of the ciliate, the distance between two kineties is approximately 1 μ in the mature trophont and 1.5 μ in the theront. Despite considerable changes of the value of the surface, the distance between two kineties remains approximately constant.

What is the mechanism of the variation of the number of kineties? We may start from the theront, the kineties of which are practically bipolar. During the growth, some kineties are interrupted; a multiplication of kinetosomes takes place. Ramifications are produced, and the new branches find their place between two other kineties. Thus, new kineties are formed during the increase of the surface of the cortex. During palintomy, short sectors of kineties are to be seen on the surface of the tomont. The division of the ciliate is accompanied not by a division of bipolar kineties, but by an apportionment of segments of kineties. The result is, at each generation, a reduction of the number of kineties. It is only after the last division that the tomite regularizes its ciliary system, which becomes bipolar. Thus, in *Ichthyophthirius,* there is no genetical continuity of kineties, but reorganization of kinetosomal material in longitudinal kineties. And the nature of cortex equilibrium is such that throughout the cycle, despite considerable variations of size and owing to a constant change of the number of kineties, the distance between two kineties remains constant. Things happen as if the number of kinetosomes per surface unit were more or less constant.

The constancy of the cortical pattern is not the sole result of the perpetuation of autonomous populations of kinetosomes or of specific kineties. It appears to be the result of the response of an apparently homogeneous population of kinetosomes to their environment.

# CHAPTER 7

## Order and Disorder; Torsion and Detorsion

When considering the different phases of the life cycle of apostomatous ciliates, one is struck by the alternation of spiral and meridian stages. This is especially striking in *Foettingeria,* and thus we are naturally led to the problem of torsion and asymmetry. Before discussing this problem, let us say a few words concerning the kinetodesma.

As already stated, the kinety is essentially a line of kinetosomes with a kinetodesma at their right. The origin of the kinetodesma is not clear. But in the trophont of *Foettingeria* where the kinetodesma is, in some of its parts, relatively large, it shows a fibrillar structure and the kinetosomes seem to be in continuity with the fibers, that is to say, to be attached to the kinetodesma. It is known that kinetosomes of flagellates often produce fibers. It is therefore possible, and probable, that the kinetodesma represents fibers of kinetosomal origin.

Whatever its origin may be, the kinetodesma seems to play an important role in morphogenesis. In the trophont of the apostomatous ciliate *Traumatiophtora punctata,* an anarchic field of kinetosomes is always present between the anterior sectors of the rows 10 and 1. The row 11 starts somewhat lower. Obviously, the kinetosomes of the anarchic field represent the kinetosomes of the anterior sector of the kinety 11. This conclusion is reinforced by the fact that these kinetosomes are paired, as are always the kinetosomes of the anterior sectors of the rows $n$ and $n - 1$ (in this case $n = 11$).

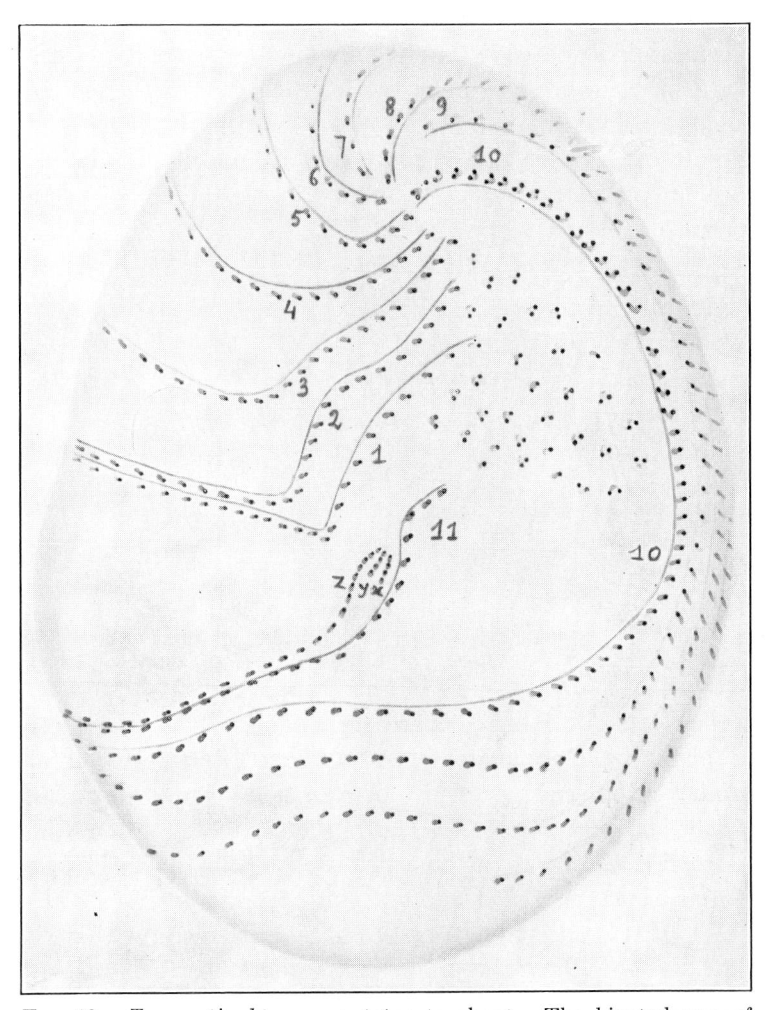


FIG. 19. *Traumatiophtora punctata:* trophont. The kinetodesma of the anterior part of kinety 11 has disappeared. The kinetosomes of the anterior part of 11 are scattered in disorder. They exhibit a double structure, just as the granule of the anterior part of 10—remainder of the tomital "falciform field."

In the region where 11 exists as a row, a kinetodesma is visible. There is no kinetodesma further up. The kinetodesma has disappeared, and it seems highly probable that its disappearance is responsible for the scattering of kinetosomes. The kinetodesma appears as the framework of kinetosomal order, the visible agent by which the hitherto unknown "morphogenetic forces" exert their mysterious orienting action.

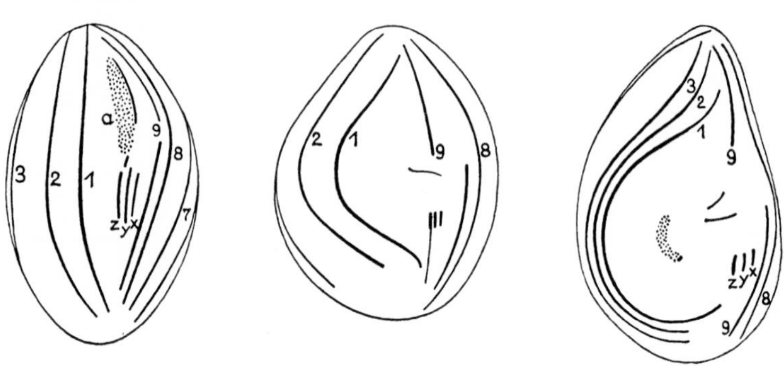


Fig. 20. *Phoretophrya nebaliae.* Formation of the hypertomite, showing the elongation of kineties 1, 2, 3.

During morphogenesis of the trophont of *Phoretophrya nebaliae,* some kineties increase in length. Is this purely a passive phenomenon, corresponding to the stretching, under cytoplasmic pressure, of a fiber, anchored at its anterior and posterior ends? Or is the stretching active, that is to say, the result of elongation of certain fibers by synthesis of new material? The latter hypothesis seems plausible. If it is admitted, it is also necessary to admit that the unequal growth of the different kinetodesmas is the expression of an unequal distribution of the substances inducing the growth of kinetodesmal fibers. Nevertheless, the unequal development of kinetodesmas, even if it is held responsible for the torsion, cannot be the cause of asymmetry; it would rather be an effect of this asymmetry.

Let us consider now a more remarkable example of torsion.

*Foettingeria* lives in the gastrovascular fluid of coelenterates. The size of the trophont varies from 20 to 600 $\mu$. Its structure shows nothing remarkable.

If the trophont, whatever its size may be, is taken out of

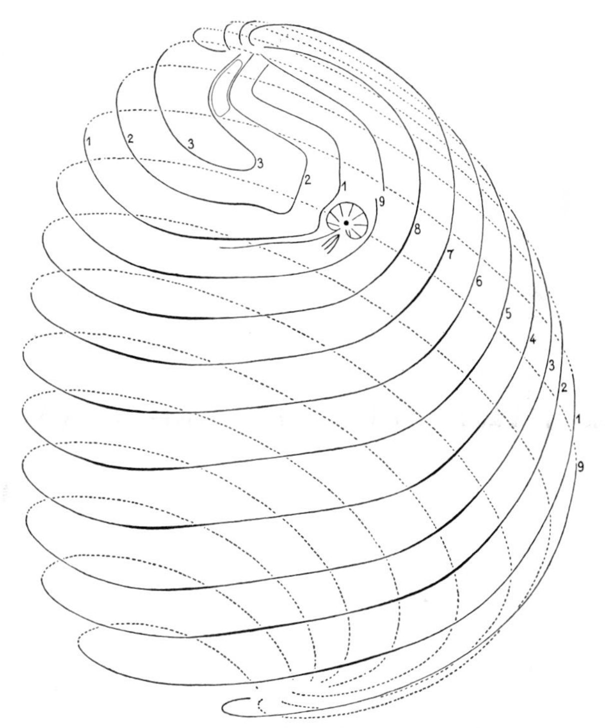


FIG. 21. *Foettingeria actiniarum:* trophont.

the *Actinia,* it encysts and undergoes a detorsion. Very early, the kinetosomes of the row 1 produce by division a field of granules which is then oriented in one, and later on in three, rows. A perfectly bipolar structure is produced. Division starts and produces some thousands of tomites. The formation of the tomite is somewhat more complicated than in the other species. The rows $x$, $y$, $z$ are reduced progressively to the size they will have in the *trophont,* but at

FIG. 22. *Foettingeria actiniarum:* detorsion and palintomy.

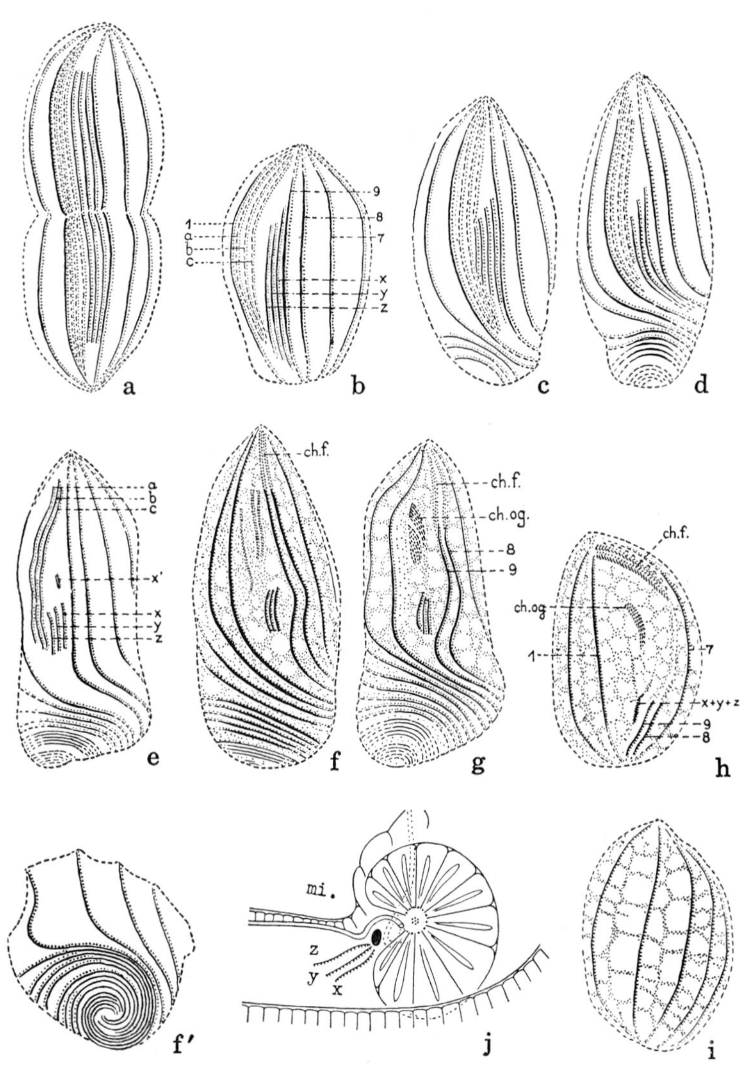


FIG. 23. *Foettingeria actiniarum:* tomitogenesis. (a) Last division. (b)–(g) Regression of $x$, $y$, $z$. Formation of the ogival and falciform fields. Torsion. (h)–(i) The tomite. The posterior spiral coil has been invaginated. (j) The rosette, formed from $x'$, as seen in the trophont.

the same time the other ciliary rows are rolled up at the posterior end into a sinistral spiral coil. This spiral coil then suddenly disappears. It has been invaginated into the posterior end. This apart, the tomite shows nothing remarkable. The anterior part of the row $x$ will give rise to

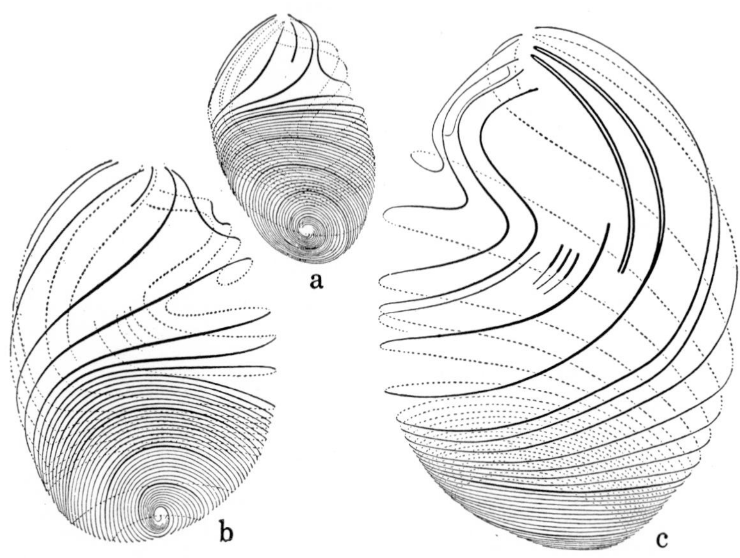


FIG. 24. *Foettingeria actiniarum.* Growth of the trophont. The detorsion accompanying the increase of size is clearly visible. The smallest trophont (a) is 29 $\mu$ long. The largest (c) is 60 $\mu$. Compare with the 160-$\mu$-long trophont of Fig. 21.

the rosette or mouth organ which has the same structure and size in the tomite as in the adult. The spiral coil formed and invaginated during the tomitogenesis of *Foettingeria* will be extruded during the phoretic phase. But the extruded spiral will be dextral, that is to say, have an inverted direction. Thus it is obvious that torsions of the cytoplasm may take place independently of elongation of kinetodesmas.

This is certainly a very rare, if not unique, example of the succession of a dextral and sinistral structure in one organism. In the gastropod *Limnaea peregrea,* the dextral or sinistral torsion is controlled by a pair of allelomorphic genes. In *Foettingeria* dextral and sinistral torsions do not

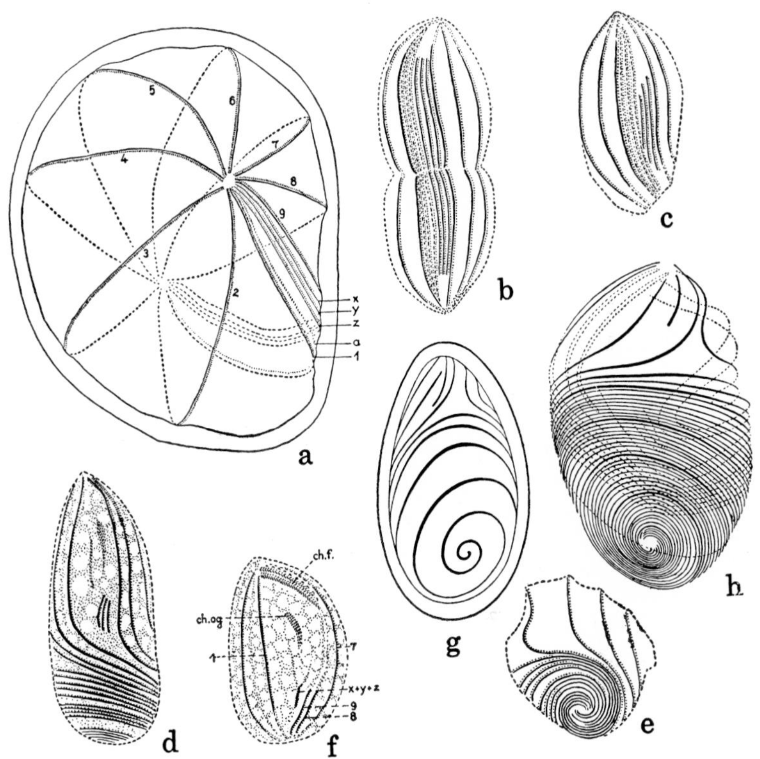


FIG. 25. *Foettingeria actiniarum:* different aspects of the ciliary system. (a) Median protomont. (b) Last division. (c) Torsion of the protomite. (d) Protomite. (e) Posterior pole of the protomite. (f) Tomite. (g) Encysted phoront. The invaginated spiral coil has been devaginated. (h) Young trophont. The torsion in the phoront (g) and trophont (h) are inverse of the protomital torsion (e).

reflect different genomes, but are the response to definite phases of the life cycle.

During the trophic phase, changes of the superficial architecture consist essentially in the unrolling of the kinetodesmas. Before division, the enrolled ciliature of the tro-phont becomes meridian, which means an important shortening.

It is possible to describe the morphology of ciliates in terms of kinetosomes and their derivatives. The morpho-genesis of a ciliate is essentially the multiplication, distribu-tion, and organization of populations of kinetosomes and of the organelles which are the result of their activity. Kineto-somal order is controlled, at least partially, by the kineto-desmas. Embryologists have been led to postulate the ex-istence of specific patterns of protein molecules or fibers which would appear during embryonic development and play an important role in morphogenesis. F. O. Schmitt (1941) has in vain tried to obtain evidence for this type of structure. The study of apostomatous Protozoa shows that such fibers do exist and that they play, at least in ciliates, an effective role in morphogenetic processes.

As these fibers undergo unequal growth during develop-ment, we have to predicate an asymmetrical distribution of the substances controlling the synthesis of the fibrous mate-rial. But, evidently, the problem of asymmetry has been only pushed back, and we have studied the results of asym-metry rather than its cause.

Finally, we have to recall once more that kinetodesmas are asymmetrical fibers. The problem of the origin of this asymmetry still awaits its solution, just like the problem of the spiral structure of cellulose fibers or of starch molecules.

CHAPTER 8

# Problems of Equilibrium

If dividing *Leucophrys piriformis* are treated with a hypertonic solution [E. Chatton (1921)], the constriction is inhibited. The proter and the opisthe may fuse in such a way that the two stomatogenic meridians are back to back. The monster has a double set of somatic kineties, two mouths, one macronucleus, and one or two micronuclei. According to E. Fauré-Frémiet (1948a), the stability of the "doublet" of *Leucophrys patula* is bound to the maintenance of axial symmetry. If any asymmetric phenomena occur during division, if for example one mouth is lost, the result will be a ciliate possessing one mouth and two sets of kineties. Then, progressively, the number of kineties will diminish and go back to the original number. The nuclear duality, when it exists, disappears, and finally the normal, original structure is obtained.

But it happens sometimes that non-disjunction of the proter and opisthe leads to heteropolar monsters, which are able to feed and to grow, but not to divide, and which finally cytolyse. In these heteropolar monsters, the kineties diverge from two or more poles and their elongation gives rise to multipolar systems. According to Fauré-Frémiet, there is a "geometrical impossibility" of the formation of a division zone separating two systems of homogeneous and homopolar kineties. It must not be forgotten that kineties, according to the law of desmodexy, are dissymmetric structures. The kinetial system is compared by Fauré-Frémiet to a "crystalline network" or to the "complex mesh of a supermolecular structure of the crystalline type." Fauré-

Frémiet (1948*b*) considers that "it is the ciliary system, or, more precisely, the infraciliature in the sense of Chatton and Lwoff, which commands all the regenerative morphogenesis." Let us recall that the infraciliature is the sum of kinetosomes.

The study of morphogenesis, in very evolved ciliates, e.g., *Licnophora* and *Euplotes,* will show later how, starting from kinetosomes and other non-visible materials, a specific complicated structure may be formed. Kinetosomes are the instruments of morphogenesis. The importance of the infraciliature is therefore not questionable. However, I should like to point out that, if kinetosomes are necessary for morphogenesis, they seem not to "command" but to obey some mysterious force which is responsible for their orientation. Perhaps it is better to say that they cooperate with some other factors, or that morphogenesis is the result of the interaction of kinetosomes with other factors. This problem will be discussed later on.

Coming back to the problem of symmetry and equilibrium, I should like to add a few remarks to Fauré-Frémiet's important experiments and discussion. The cortical pattern and especially the kinetial system are certainly important. When considering many evolved ciliates and especially the group of *Thigmotricha,* it is clear that the division "zone" does not coincide with the theoretical equator of the organism, but "cuts" the kineties in their middle, even if they are located on the anterior half of the parent [E. Chatton and A. Lwoff (1949)]. The question naturally arises, and this is not a purely academic discussion, whether it is not the middle of the kinety which determines the position of the constriction zone. This would mean a more or less "autonomous" equilibrium of the kinety. But studies of apostomes have shown that the length of the kinety is controlled by its environment, that is to say, by properties of the cortex as a reflection of the metabolism.

Therefore, the fact that kineties are cut in two equal parts would mean that the middle of the kinety corresponds to the middle of the underlying "morphogenetic field."

The division of a ciliate into two equal parts is the most

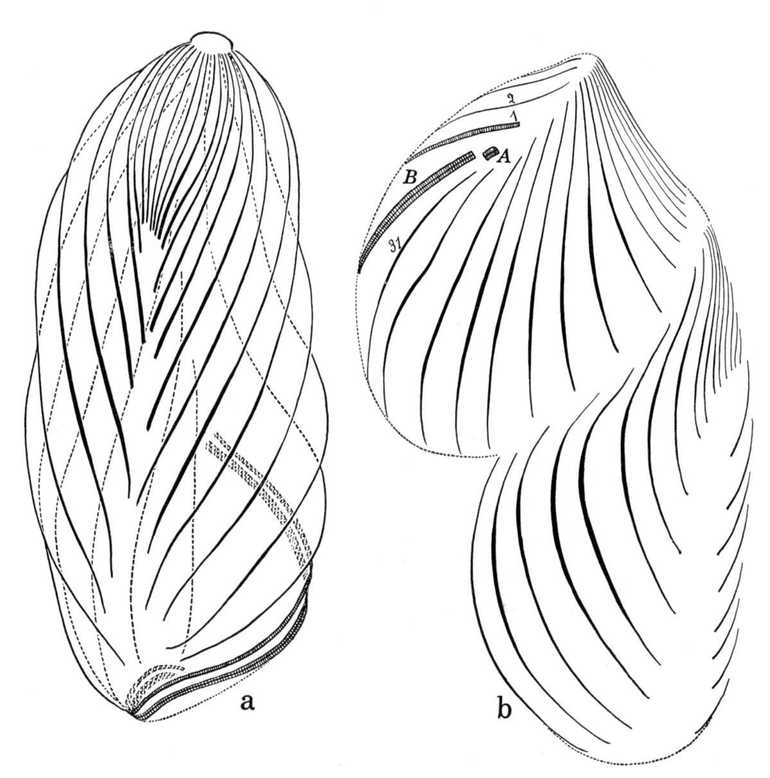


FIG. 26. *Plagiospira crinita.* (a) Dorsal view, showing the short thigmotactic kineties. (b) Division. The thigmotactic kineties are cut in their middle by the oblique striction zone. *A* and *B*, preoral kineties.

common and certainly the primitive condition. But some ciliates produce a bud, that is to say, a small opisthe. This happens in many parasitic ciliates or in suctorians which feed for long periods on other ciliates and are, if considered from a nutritional point of view, "biochemical parasites" [see A. Lwoff (1944)].

When in such parasites kineties are present and bipolar, they are cut not in their middle, but far behind the equator of the animal. In *Chromidina elegans,* for example, which is attached to the epithelium of the kidney of *Sepia elegans* by its anterior pole, the first constriction zone separates a fragment one-tenth of the length of the animal. If we consider the form of the ciliate with its enlarged anterior extremity, the volume of this fragment is far less than one-thousandth of the volume of the parent. The detached posterior part will undergo four to five divisions. At each division, the constriction zone lies behind the equator.

The combination of fixation and of some nutritional factors has resulted in the shifting towards the posterior end of the normally equatorial constriction zone. We could express this in terms of an inhibition "gradient." However, considering the fact that all segments are unequal, one is tempted to ascribe this "heterotomy" to a heterogeneous structure of the cortex with properties varying progressively from the anterior to the posterior pole. The constantly flowing endoplasm of the ciliate cannot be considered responsible for this phenomenon. The fact that trichocysts are formed only in the vicinity of the posterior end shows that the "morphogenetic substance" responsible for trichocyst formation is localized, whether formed or adsorbed we do not know, in the region where division will take place. This can be understood only if we admit that the cortexes of the anterior and posterior parts are different.

The fact that heterotomy (or budding) also takes place in suctorians where no kinetodesmas have been detected seems to show, if kinetodesmas are really absent, that the fibers express, rather than control, the properties of the cortex.

# CHAPTER 9

## The Cortical Network of Suctorians; Reproduction and Organization

Adult suctorians are devoid of cilia. They feed by numerous sucking extensions. The non-ciliated parent produces a ciliated daughter organism generally referred to as an embryo or bud.

The origin of the cilia of the embryo in this group of organisms was, for a very long time, one of the problems of protozoology. It was solved by the study of *Podophrya fixa* [E. Chatton, A. and M. Lwoff, and L. Tellier (1929)]. On the surface of the adult are numerous kinetosomes which are scattered all over an irregular network. The first sign of reproduction is the multiplication of these granules in one region of the adult. The kinetosomes become aligned in regular rows, and the hitherto irregular network is now formed, in this region only, of square units which are also regularly aligned. Cilia are produced only by the kinetosomes of this organized field.

It is obvious that the kinetosomes of this region are submitted to conditions which induce their multiplication and that some forces, or fibers, must arise which orientate the network and the kinetosomes.

A closely related species, *Podophrya parasitica,* has been examined by E. Fauré-Frémiet (1945b). It lives as parasite on the surface of ciliates and also produces ciliated embryos. However, when the host is exhausted, lines of kinetosomes are formed, not only on one area, but all around the suctorian, and cilia are produced. The adult as a whole is thus transformed into a huge "embryo." The change takes

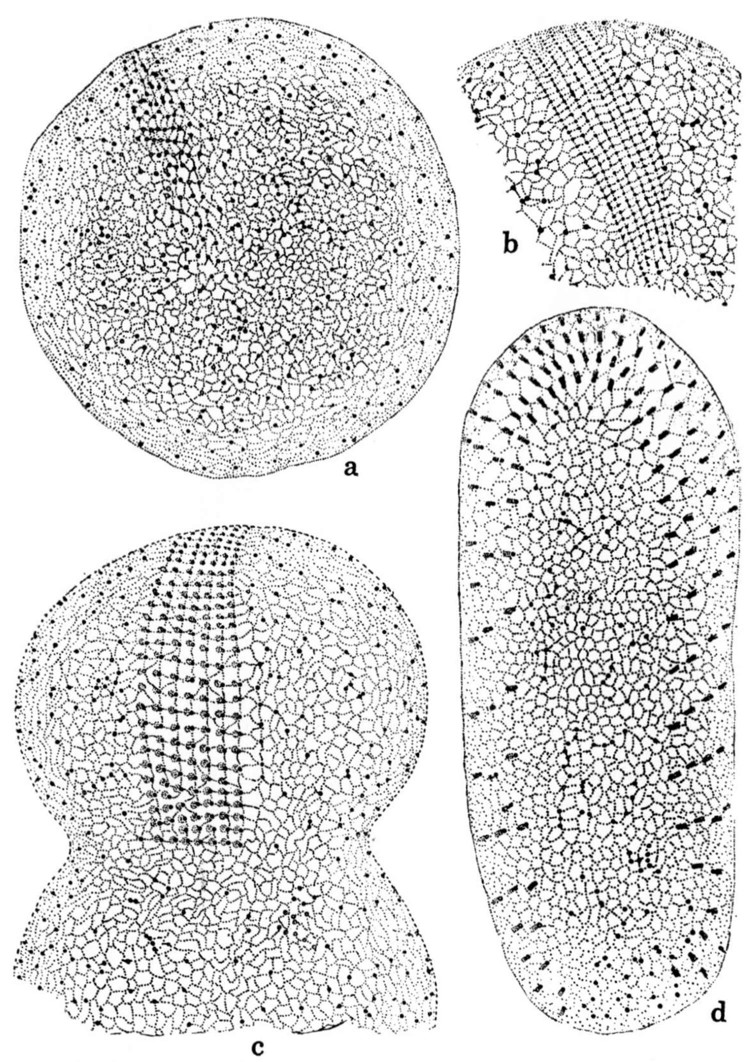


FIG. 27. *Podophrya fixa.* (a) Adult. Beginning of the formation of the embryonic field. (b) and (c) Organization of the kinetosomes of the embryonic field and of the meshes of the cortical network. (d) The embryo.

place independently of any division. It appears therefore that the arrangement of kinetosomes and the production of cilia are controlled by the nutrition. When the ciliate feeds,

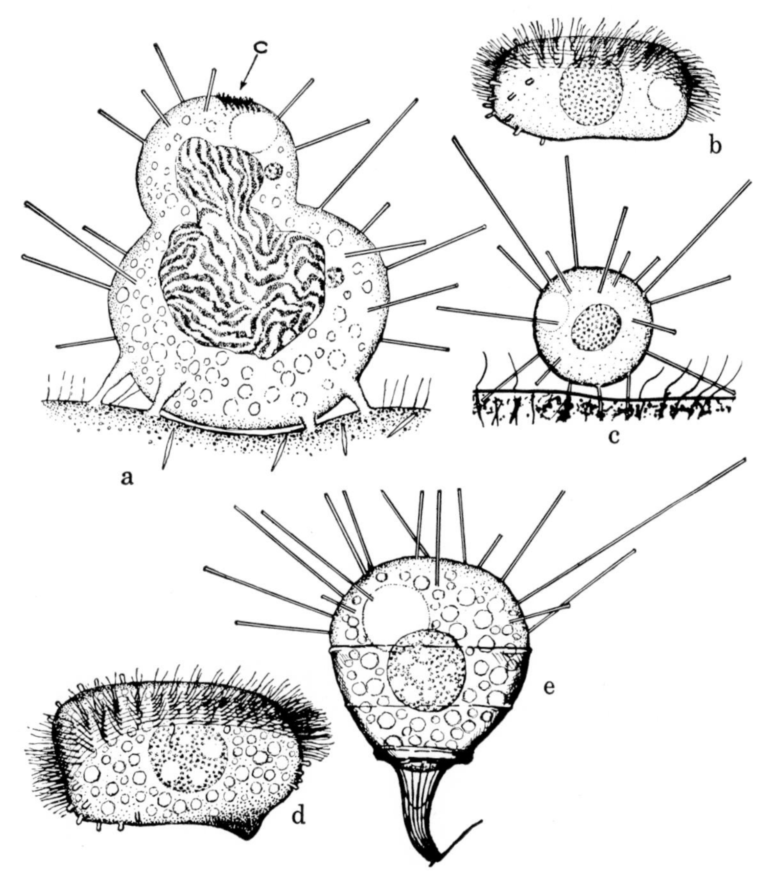


FIG. 28. *Podophrya parasitica*. (a) Adult and embryo. (b) Free embryo. (c) Newly fixed embryo. (d) Embryo resulting from the total transformation of an adult. (e) *"Tokophrya"* form.

kinetosomes are organized and produce cilia only in one region, which becomes the surface of the embryo. When the nutrition ceases, the adult as a whole is organized and produces cilia.

From the evolutionary point of view, it is worth noticing that the ciliated phase is phylogenetically the primitive one. The production of the "embryo," characterized by the organization of the anarchic superficial network into a regular pattern, the lining up of kinetosomes, and the production of cilia, corresponds to the transitory return to a primitive condition, or, better, to the cyclical reappearance of some of the features of *Podophrya's* ancestor.

The structures which develop before division, either in the parent as a whole or only in the embryo or opisthe, are characteristic of a phylogenetically primitive condition.

## CHAPTER 10

# Movements of the Ciliary System in Ontogeny and Phylogeny

An interesting and homogeneous group of ciliates lives in the mantle cavity of bivalve molluscs. Among them is the family of *Hemispeiridae* (= *Ancistrumidae*). The somatic system of kineties is formed by longitudinal anteroposterior rows with short cilia. A small sector of this somatic system is thigmotactic. The preoral and oral systems are formed by two long curved rows, having very long cilia, and ending in the posterior oral infundibulum.

The three genera *Ancistrum, Proboveria,* and *Boveria* are characterized and defined by the position of the origin of the preoral system: anterior in *Ancistrum,* median in *Proboveria,* posterior in *Boveria*. These three genera represent three steps of an orthogenetic evolution: *Ancistrum* being the primitive type, *Proboveria* intermediate, and *Boveria* extreme [E. Chatton and A. Lwoff (1949)].

We shall first examine the division of *Proboveria*. Before any visible sign of cytoplasmic constriction, the somatic kineties are cut approximately in their middle. The oral system has migrated towards the anterior pole. The kineties have become elongated and the kinetosomes have multiplied. The kinety 1, which is stomatogenic, will give rise to various kineties: kinety *B* and pharyngeal kineties. When the morphogenesis of the preoral and oral systems is completed and when the proter and the opisthe are ready to separate, they show the typical structure of the genus *Ancistrum*. During growth, the preoral and oral systems will migrate towards the posterior pole. The adult structure is thus formed.

In *Boveria,* the preoral system is entirely rolled up "on"

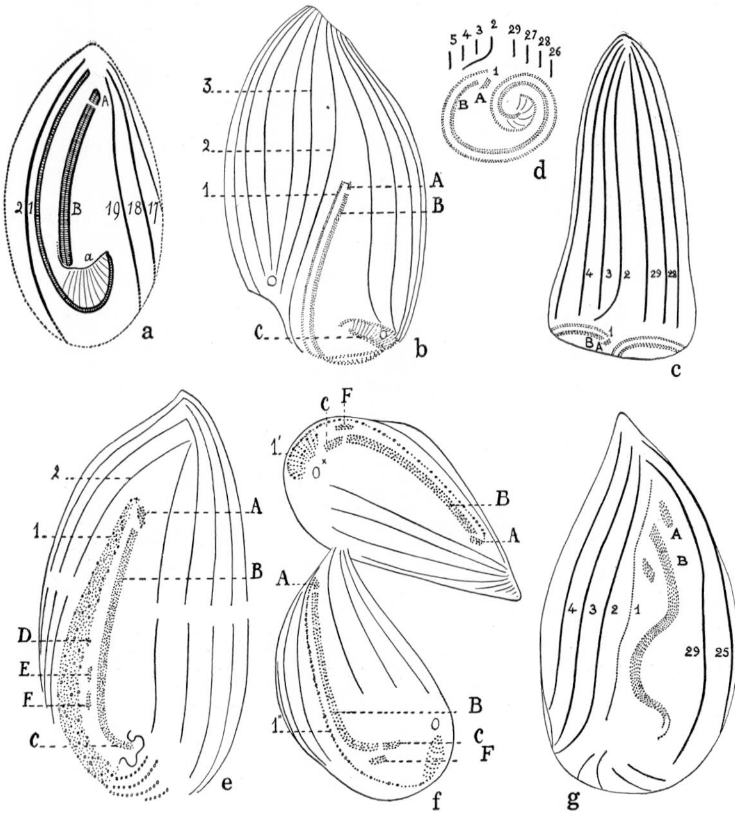


FIG. 29. Evolution of *Hemispeiridae.* (a) *Ancistrum tellinae.* (b) *Proboveria loripedis.* (c) *Boveria* (schematic). (d) Posteroventral view of *Boveria,* showing the oral system. (e), (f) Division of *Proboveria.* Note the resemblance of the daughter ciliates to the adult *Ancistrum.* (g) Predivision of *Boveria,* showing the anterior position of the oral ciliature. *A* to *F,* various preoral and oral kineties.

the posterior "pole" which has been modelled into a circular surface. Before division takes place, the totality of the preoral system migrates towards the anterior end and forms an anteroposterior band. The phenomena, if not identical with, are very similar to, those taking place in *Proboveria*.

*Ancistrum, Proboveria,* and *Boveria* are obviously closely related forms from the biological, morphological, cytological, and developmental points of view. The position of the origin of the preoral system is the main difference. As a matter of fact, this position varies somewhat in some species of *Ancistrum*.

It is difficult to escape the feeling that *Hemispeiridae* represents a monophyletic group and that *Proboveria* and *Boveria* have originated from a common ancestor of the *Ancistrum* type, which is the primitive structural form of the family.

Let us assume that the position of the oral system is the consequence of "properties" of the cortex. We have to admit that, before division, constitution and structure of the cortex, as judged by its effects on the oral system, are equivalent to those of the primitive type.

The evolutionary series—*Ancistrum* → *Proboveria* → *Boveria*—consists in an anteroposterior migration of the oral system which becomes enrolled on the posterior end. This migration is reversed before division. The predivisional type of structure corresponds to the phylogenetically primitive state; the adult's structure, by definition, to the evolved state. The movements of the oral system therefore appear as the consequence of reversible changes of cytoplasmic properties.

Evolution is generally considered to be irreversible. What is irreversible in the ciliates we are considering is the position of the preoral cilia in the mature ciliate, which is the result of ontogeny as modified by evolution. But before division, the preoral system moves towards the anterior pole. This movement is reversible. What is irreversible is the structure considered at a given phase of the life cycle. The consideration of apostomatous ciliates leads to the same conclusion.

It is generally admitted by protozoologists that one type, if not *the* type, of primitive ciliate is the *Prorodon* type. It has an anterior mouth, and diverging from it, a regular set of anteroposterior longitudinal ciliary rows. The symmetry of the cortex is axial. This hypothetically primitive type has been altered by the asymmetric development and regression of some parts of the ciliary system, by the migrations of the mouth, and by the development or alterations of the oral system. A "ventral" and a "dorsal" face can be recognized in many ciliates—for example, in *Gymnodinioides* or *Foettingeria.* But before division, a detorsion takes place. The mouth disappears. The short postoral rows become bipolar. The regular, bipolar, non-differentiated anteroposterior ciliary system of the tomont corresponds obviously to a primitive type of organization. And here again, the primitive condition is regained before each division.

Before discussing these facts we have to consider some other types of ciliates, in which it is difficult to recognize primitive and evolved features but which will provide good material for concluding this discussion.

# CHAPTER 11

## Differentiation in Ciliates

Development of an organism, as already stated, may be considered from the angle of cell diversification. Is it possible to trace homologous phenomena among ciliates? To what extent are differences of the various sectors of a ciliate equivalent to cell differentiation?

In apostomatous ciliates, these differences are, at least partially, responsible for the specific structure of the ciliary system. But, by definition, differentiation is not reversible. And there often exists in cells of higher organisms a marked antagonism between differentiation and division. Many differentiated cells are unable to divide. Since ciliates divide, one could be tempted to conclude that ontogenesis of ciliates has in common with ontogenesis of Metazoa only its quality of ontogenesis. Let us compare the morphogenetical processes in some ciliates.

In ciliates of the *Leucophrys* type, the proter and the opisthe are modelled in the anterior and posterior parts of the parent. The infra-equatorial part, between the kinety 1 (stomatogenic) and the last kinety *n*, becomes the oral zone of the opisthe. In this case, apparently, no element of the cortex has undergone irreversible change.

In the hypotrichous ciliate *Euplotes,* the argyrophylic cortical network is entirely reorganized at each division, starting from non-visible building blocks.

The oral ciliature of the opisthe will be formed by division and organization of an anarchic field of kinetosomes. The old parental structures disappear; cortical network and cirri are reorganized: the parental mouth is reorganized into the proter's mouth. As has been correctly noted by V. Tartar (1941), "Clearly differentiation and dedifferentiation are here not conditions which characterize the cell as a

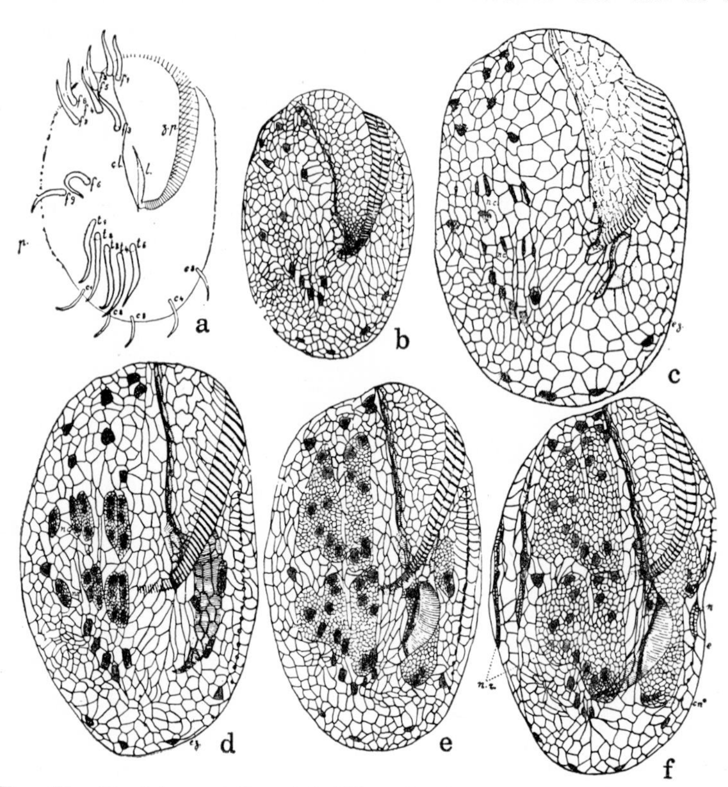

FIG. 30. *Euplotes patella.* (a) Ciliate *in vivo.* $c_1$–$c_5$, posterior cirrhi; *c.l.*, longitudinal crest; $f_1$–$f_9$, frontal cirrhi; *l.*, undulating membrane; *p.*, pulsola; $t_1$–$t_5$, transverse cirrhi; *z.p.*, preoral zone. (b) Young ciliate. (c)–(f) Predividing form, showing the new cirrhi and new network. The peristome of the opisthe is formed from one kinetosome originating from the posterior sector of the parental peristome. *e.z.*, developing oral zone of the opisthe; *n.c.*, new cirrhi; *n.z.*, new network.

whole but are quite local events which may occur simultaneously in different regions of the cell." It is quite obvious that many organelles are unable to divide. The "rosette" of the apostomes lacks this ability. A new rosette has to be formed anew from the kinety $x$ in each tomite. And the mouth of many ciliates behaves in the same way. Differentiated organelles are very often unable to divide.

According to Tartar, "Ciliates show in a dramatic way that cell division is not incompatible with differentiation. The division period is in fact just the time of greatest formation of new structures and the two processes of morphogenesis and division run parallel in time."

Of course, if differentiation is by definition considered incompatible with cell division, ciliates are not differentiated organisms. But the interval of time between two divisions of *Euplotes* is 24 hours, and the morphogenetic processes start 8 hours before the cytoplasmic cleavage. As a matter of fact, "division" is a very complicated process. Two new "morphogenetic fields" are formed which organize the proter and the opisthe in the anterior and posterior parts of the parent. The differentiated structures of the parent then disappear. "Division" *stricto sensu* separates two highly differentiated ciliates. The important phenomenon and the great mystery in this division are the formation a long time before nuclear division of two "morphogenetic fields." It is quite obvious that it is not a "differentiated" ciliate which "divides" but that cleavage separates two already highly differentiated ciliates. The real division has taken place 8 hours before, at the time where two new morphogenetic fields have appeared. Although the old, differentiated, parental structure is still there at this period, it is nevertheless a dead structure, sentenced to dissolution and disappearance. It is therefore clear that the term "differentiation," considered as an irreversible modification of a cell, cannot be applied without discussion to a non-cellular organism.

Differentiation in ciliates is synonymous with changes occurring during morphogenesis or development. But this organization, when considered independently of the phase of the life cycle, is reversible. It is reversible because it represents essentially the sum of the movements of the kinetosomes. Two new "daughter-patterns" are formed anew at each generation from one or many kinetosomes. The adult ciliate is homologous to an adult organism. The "predividing" ciliate is, to a certain extent, homologous to an egg. Let us remember that most of the apostomes can divide only in the encysted stage, that is to say, after production, like an egg of one, or even two, cystic membranes. Let us remember also that the hypertomite of *Phoretophrya* and the hypertrophont of *Synophrya* divide only some hours before the ecdysis of the host. Their division is controlled by an external stimulus and thereby recalls the activation of the egg.

We have to remember that before each division the oral kineties of *Proboveria* and *Boveria* migrate towards the anterior pole and take up a phylogenetically primitive position. The situation is here very favorable because the phylogenetic change we have considered is not a morphological "differentiation" but only a change in the position of a system. The conditions, whatever they may be, which are responsible for the movements and equilibrium of the oral structures on the cortex are the result of the changes which take place after division. Some phylogenetically primitive condition reappears before each division. The study of apostomatous ciliates in which a bipolar meridian pattern is produced before division has already allowed the same conclusion. The differentiated cortex of highly evolved ciliates may thus be compared to the differentiated cells of a metazoan. The "neutral" cytoplasm and the self-reproducing units such as kinetosomes may be compared to the germinal line, in the sense that they are responsible for the "creation" of new organisms.

Thus, if we consider highly evolved ciliates, we see that the "adult" is unable to undergo division. There is really an antagonism between differentiation, in the sense of complex productions of the adult, and division.

The ciliates have solved the problem of perpetuating complex adult structure by cyclical dedifferentiation. The life cycle of a ciliate is such that, after a certain period of growth, something is changed in the unstable equilibrium of some systems. The old structures disappear and the properties of the predividing organism are such that phylogenetically primitive conditions and corresponding structures are formed.

Data on the chemistry of cell division are scarce. L. Rapkine has shown that in the sea-urchin egg, before division, there is a considerable increase of the —SH groups. This has been extended to apostomatous ciliates [E. Chatton, A. Lwoff, and L. Rapkine (1931)]. But, except for this, we have no data on the nature of the changes, and it appears of utmost importance to obtain information concerning enzymatic activities preceding division in ciliates.

CHAPTER 12

# Interactions of Morphogenetic Units

The process of orderly organization of the cortical network of *Podophrya parasitica* which we have described is, according to E. Fauré-Frémiet (1945a), "the transition between an amorphous state to an orderly state as if space lattice forces have been responsible for a crystallization." We do not know yet whether the meshes of the parental network disappear and are replaced by new structures or are simply reshaped. The latter hypothesis seems to correspond to the facts. Whatever the case may be, meshes exist in the cortical network of the adult *Podophrya*, but are differently arranged from those in the embryo. What is the nature of the change? This is certainly an important problem.

The ciliate *Sphenophrya dosiniae* possesses a sucker which undergoes a considerable development. The organism is apparently stretched by this rigid structure. In the mature ciliate, the posterior "pole," that is to say, the point where the posterior ends of the kineties join, is located approximately on the middle of one "face." The cortical network is very irregular. Some meshes are small and more or less regularly penta- or hexagonal; some, especially in the posterior region, are considerably longer, just as if the surface had been stretched. These are indications of some elasticity of the surface during the growth of the organism. But if the meshes were just elastic, their size and shape would be regularized after completion of the growth. This is not the case. Things happen as if "tension forces" were acting continuously, or as if meshes, extensible during development, had turned into a rigid structure after the maximal size was reached.

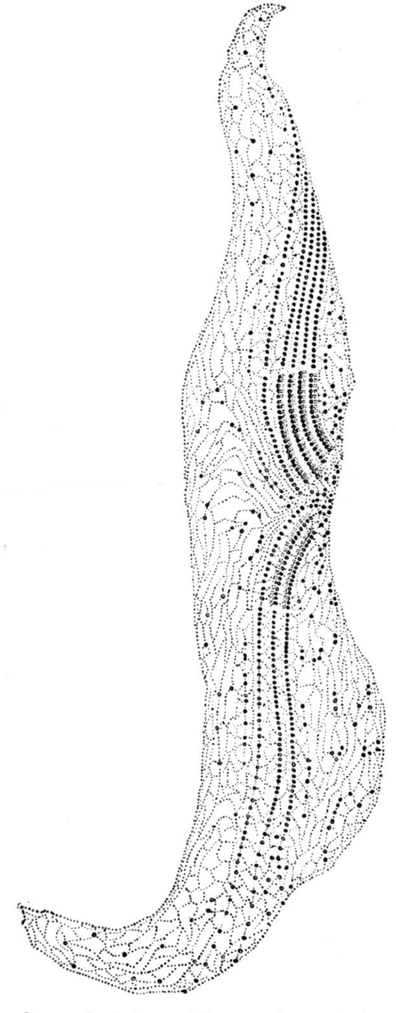

FIG. 31. *Sphenophrya dosiniae.* The meshes of the cortical network are very elongated in the vicinity of the posterior region (between the V formed by the posterior sectors of the ciliary system).

The large network of an adult *Euplotes* also seems a rigid structure, able to disappear only when replaced by the newly formed meshes which enlarge or "grow" during morphogenesis of the daughter organisms. The "rigidity" of the differentiated network is shown by starvation experiments with the hypotrich *Stylonychia mytilus,* during which the size of the organism decreases. The organism is repeatedly reorganized into a smaller organism during this process [Dembowska (1938)].

We encounter great difficulties when we try to define what may be considered as specific phenomena of a dividing ciliate from the purely morphological point of view.

To analyze division in a very simple organism like a primitive flagellate possessing one flagellum seems easy. Division of the kinetosome is one of the first visible signs, and precedes nuclear and cytoplasmic division. Some conditions induce the division of one self-reproducing organelle. But this does not mean that the division of self-reproducing organelles is responsible for the division of the organism.

In *Gymnodinioides,* elongation of kineties *a, x, y, z* takes place before division and seems "specific" of division. Obviously, some morphogenetic material induces the division of the kinetosomes of these four ciliary rows. Synthesis of some "morphogenetic material" thus appears as one of the important phenomena preceding division. But one could object that in regeneration also there is synthesis of morphogenetic material. This is true.

Nevertheless, we may consider the complex association of the cortical network with kinetosomes. The cortical network, as has been shown, is a rigid structure in highly evolved mature ciliates. On the contrary, kinetosomes may multiply and increase in number as do other particles endowed with genetic continuity.

We know that something in the cortical structure orients the kinetosomes and the kinetodesmas. What may be the relations of such an "orienting system" to the oriented material?

If something orientates kinetosomes, it can be only by virtue of some electronic or intermolecular forces. Let us admit the hypothesis that the orienting system of an adult ciliate is a rigid structure, unable to grow beyond certain limits, as are the meshes of the cortical network. If the kinetosomes continue to increase in number, the "reactive groups" of the orienting system will finally become "saturated." The newly formed kinetosomes will find no place to attach themselves. Their position will no longer be controlled.

But if kinetosomes are normally bound to the orienting system by electronic forces, this means that they have also "reactive groups." Kinetosomes which are not bound to the orienting system have *ipso facto* "non-saturated bonds" able to attract or to aggregate free building blocks of the orienting system. The free blocks would result from continued synthesis after the size limit of the orienting system was reached. These blocks will now crystallize according to their structure and environment and form new systems or new organelles. We can propose as an example of this type of phenomenon the attracting and orienting action of the kinetosome in so many metazoan cells or Protozoa. Certainly if one kinetosome is able to exert such an influence, groups of kinetosomes may have also a powerful action.

In ciliates it is certain that multiplication of kinetosomes precedes organization. The oral system, the membranelles of *Leucophrys* or of *Licnophora,* are modelled in anarchic kinetosomal fields. The cortical network of *Euplotes* is formed around the newly formed fields of kinetosomes which will produce the cirri. Strangely enough, the cortical network of the ventral face of *Euplotes* develops separately around the eight newly formed cirri. There is not *one* morphogenetic field for each daughter cell, but a series of fields which will then fuse harmoniously into the characteristic pattern of the parent.

Of course, when one tries to find what is really specific of division, the only possible answer is: the duplication of the differentiated structures, or the partial or total substitution and superposition of two differentiated structures for the unique parental structure; in other terms, the transition between an organism with one morphogenetic field into an organism with two morphogenetic fields.

In a dividing cell, with two asters surrounding kinetosomes, the daughter kinetosomes act as if repulsing each other. This model seems far too simple when we are dealing with the duplication of morphogenetic "fields." Nevertheless, the equilibrium of two interacting systems, one of them being the kinetosomal system, seems to play an important role in morphogenesis and division of ciliates. This hypothetical concept should of course be submitted to experimental control.

But I want to emphasize that this conception of interaction of two—or more—systems is able to provide an explanation of the cyclic formation of trichocysts. Let us suppose that the maximal affinity of the kinetosome is for the building blocks of the orienting system and for the building blocks of cilia. Let us suppose that more kinetosomes are formed than available units of these building blocks, or that the relative speed of their synthesis is low. This would result in "free" kinetosomes which would be able to bind material for which the affinity is low, for example, building blocks of trichocysts, the result being the formation of trichocysts.

CHAPTER 13

# Ontogeny in Ciliates and the Differentiation of Metazoan Cells

Morphogenesis of an animal may be considered the result of cell differentiation. Only the germ line remains totipotent. The other cells become specialized, and development results from the interaction of differentiated cells and from the actions and interaction of the products of specific activities of differentiated cells. An organism is the equilibrated sum of differentiated cells. One of the problems of development is the problem of the nature and origin of cell diversification and specialization.

We know that the genome as a whole is a principle of stability and that genes control enzymes. But development is the story of diversification of cells possessing the very same genome. It is convenient to visualize diversification as the result of segregation of specific cytoplasmic particles, which, with the collaboration of genes, would be responsible for the synthesis of enzymes or group of enzymes. It is possible also with P. Weiss (1949) to consider differentiation as "a chain of events consisting of alternate physical regrouping and chemical alteration of the molecular populations, the latter phenomenon involving the emergence of novel species of compounds." Whatever our opinions on differentiation may be, it happens that in many eggs deutoplasmic reserves of different types are unequally distributed. Cleavage necessarily separates blastomeres possessing different reserves, that is to say, different types of metabolism.

We know that in euglenas such as *Euglena mesnili,* the relative speed of chloroplast multiplication and of cell division may be altered in the absence of light [A. Lwoff and H. Dusi (1935)]. This is an example, or a model, allowing us to accept for the time being the hypothesis that, owing to the nature of reserves, that is to say, of metabolism, cytoplasmic corpuscles can or cannot multiply, or multiply more or less rapidly, and in some instance be lost in certain types of cells. During development of the egg of the ctenophore *Beroë* or of the mollusc *Dentalium,* substances such as "green ectoderm-producing substances" or "non-colored endoderm-producing material" are synthesized. Whether they are located in, or bound to, plasmagenes is not known. Nevertheless, as these substances are unequally distributed, cleavage brings about a segregation or localization of preformed substances. During the development of the trochophore larvae of molluscs, only some lines of cells produce cilia. Obviously, kinetosomes have multiplied and have produced cilia in certain types of cells only. Thus an organelle, the kinetosome, endowed with genetic continuity may behave differently in different cells of an animal, just as it behaves differently in different parts of a ciliate. Are these two types of "differentiation," to some extent, comparable? Differentiation in a ciliate is essentially a cortical phenomenon. To what extent is it possible to extend data concerning ciliates to other animals? Is the cortex of a ciliate something peculiar? Are the cortical phenomena which occur in ciliates the specific expression of a general law?

The importance of cell surface has been stressed by many embryologists. E. E. Just (1939) went so far as to consider that "in the entire animal kingdom, with the exception of mammals, the embryo arises from the egg surface." E. Fauré-Frémiet and H. Mugard (1948) have discovered that very important cortical phenomena take place during the development of *Teredo norvegica*. After the expulsion of the second polar corpuscle, the surface of the egg is homogeneous as far as argyrophyly is concerned. But during development, certain blastomeres show an increase of argyrophylic particles. These are the two blastomeres *X* issued from *D* and blastomeres *M* and *Y*. They will give rise to the cells of the shell gland, and to mesodermal and mesenchymatous cells. Therefore, differentiation of the blasto-

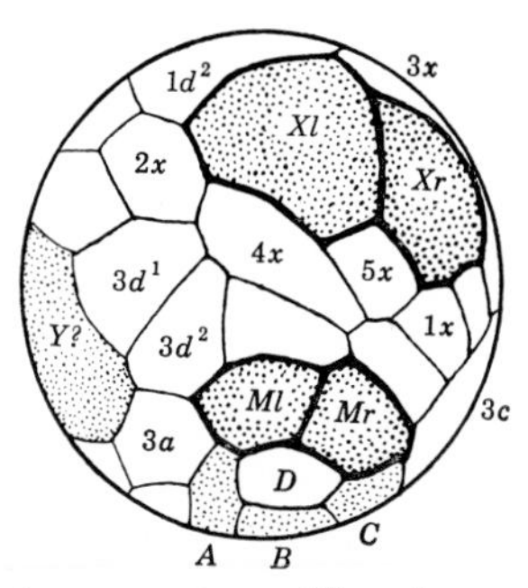


Fig. 32. *Teredo norvegica*. Silver-impregnated morula.

mere is accompanied by cortical events. These events could of course be the result as well as the cause of differentiation. But in the last analysis we are compelled to ascribe differentiation to the specific particles of the cell.

Is it possible to compare morphogenetic factors in ciliates and Metazoa? We know that many parasitic Protozoa show cytoplasmic differentiations in the region by which they feed and that in ciliates nutrition interferes with morphogenesis. Many eggs are attached to the ovary; they have therefore a trophic region. This may account for the formation of an axis. We know also, thanks to D. M. Whitaker (1940), that in *Fucus* the axis may be induced by external factors such as light.

A. L. Cohen's (1942) principle of self-increasing complexity is here very useful. According to this principle,

"Once a certain degree of complexity is introduced into a medium, the complexity will increase under its own momentum, physically, chemically, or both."

"Given just the number of asymmetrical conditions in the environment, the chemical complexity of protoplasm is sufficient to evoke further spatial patterning. This, in turn, increases the complexity of the gradients and phases and so evokes a still more complex patterning, the whole cycle repeating itself until the system has reached a condition of dynamic stability or of rigidity as in fructification. But development is a perfectly orderly phenomenon; therefore, segregation of particles must be controlled by severe and unescapable laws. This is perhaps the reason for the success of the cortical theories postulating an organization of the cortex."

I should like to say that an orderly or organized asymmetry, like that of an egg or of a ciliate, may only be the reflection of cortical properties. A constantly flowing or potentially flowing endoplasm cannot be asymmetrical. The building blocks of the different organelles may be asymmetrical; the organelles may be asymmetrical. But if we consider the ciliate as an organism, we reach the conclusion that organized asymmetry or simply organization can belong only to a more or less rigid, or more or less permanent, system, that is to say, to the cortex.

It is known that the dextral or sinistral torsion of *Limnaea* is controlled by a pair of allelomorphic genes. But the type of structure is determined not by the genetic constitution of the organism, but by that of the oöcyte from which it arose. The direction of torsion depends on some structure which is formed during the growth of the oöcyte. The hypothesis that this structure is cortical seems likely and is in agreement with A. L. Cohen's statement (1942) that "a surface is not a mathematical plane but a layer of more or less oriented molecules or atoms with fields of forces which in some instances may be quite powerful."

The cortex is certainly very important, not only because we have considered the surface of ciliates. And the conclusion that there is something in common in the ontogeny of ciliates and the differentiation of metazoan cells during development, namely, the organization of the cortex, seems, for the time being, quite reasonable.

CHAPTER 14

# The Kinetosome in Development, Morphogenesis, and Evolution

Ciliates provide a model in which a cytoplasmic unit endowed with genetic continuity and playing an important role in morphogenesis is seen at work during developmental processes. An important feature of the kinetosome is its polyvalency. The fact that one specific particle is able to synthesize types of organites as different from a functional point of view as a cilium or a trichocyst is very suggestive. Whatever the chemical parenthood of the two structures may be, the facts show the importance of such particles. Their loss or modification would bring about the disappearance of many functions. This explains perhaps the great scarcity of plasmatic inheritance. It is possible that many mutations of plasmatic particles are lethal because each particle controls many reactions.

The nature of the control of the alternative activities of a cytoplasmic unit like the kinetosome remains an acute problem. Many hypotheses may be considered when one tries to understand the possible mechanism by which a kinetosome is turned into a trichocystosome.

1. The hypothesis of a random mutation can be excluded because all the kinetosomes of one ciliate produce a trichocystosome at the same time.

2. The hypothesis of an induced mutation is difficult to admit. The kinetosome divides into two particles, one remaining a kinetosome able to produce other "normal" kinetosomes, that is to say, cilia-synthesizers. Is the difference

between the two daughter organelles the result of an induced unequational division? The kinetosome has been considered as a "unit." The evidence for doing so is only morphological, that is to say, largely insufficient. A kinetosome is large enough to be a complex of different molecular species, living together side by side and generally multiplying together. But it is possible that some conditions may favor one molecular species. The unequational division would thus correspond to an induced division of one part of the kinetosome. We can also admit that, if owing to a changed environment one molecular species has "grown" more than others, division might give rise to a "disequilibrated" or modified particle. Things look like an induced unequational division only if we consider the kinetosome as a "unit."

3. But the possibility remains that kinetosomes and trichocystosomes are in fact the product of a normal division. Their different behavior could be due to different factors:

*a.* Owing to its position far from the kinetodesma, the trichocystosome could be in slightly different environmental conditions from the kinetosome. We know that mitochondria, for example, are not equally distributed in the cortex of a ciliate [E. Chatton and S. Brachon (1935)].

*b.* The kinetosome remains attached, probably by a fiber to the kinetodesma. This fiber may perhaps modify some of its properties.

It is very difficult to make a choice among hypotheses 1, 2, and 3. It will be, in fact, impossible as long as the behavior of kinetosomes has not been submitted to an experimental analysis. This should really be attempted. However, it must be recalled that in a flagellate such as *Trichomonas* one single kinetosome is able to give rise to a flagellum, a fiber, an axostyle, and a parabasal body. These organelles may be chemically closely related, and it is possible that their production corresponds to minute changes of the metabolism of the kinetosome. But in some flagellates, as well as in some ciliates, the only product of the kinetosome is a cilium. This again may be due either to environmental differences or to differences of the constitution of the kinetosome itself. Transplantations, if they are possible, should help solve the problem. What we see, in fact, is that under apparently precise and perfectly unknown conditions one granule produces what we may consider an orientated and orderly polymerization of some material or materials (proteins, polysaccharides, lipids).

Whatever the intimate cause of the polyvalency of kinetosomes may be, the polyvalency remains. The kinetosomes themselves and their products are one mode of expression of ciliate characters. And here is perhaps the main originality of ciliates. Most structures of highly differentiated ciliates are rigid formations, unable to divide. But they are able to undergo dedifferentiation, and apparently their building blocks can be utilized again. The kinetosomes, except when they are turned into trichocystosomes, maintain their primitive features. They remain able to divide, to be organized in specific patterns together with other productions of the ciliates.

What is rigid in evolved ciliates is the sum of the kinetosomes + kinetodesmas + cortical network which constitute the specific pattern. Differentiation in a ciliate is an organization. But the properties of the whole organism are not necessarily the sum of the properties of the constituent parts. The ciliate as an organism remains totipotent, able to divide and to be reorganized. It can do this because differentiation does not affect the whole organism, but only its cortex, and because the responsible self-reproducing cytoplasmic units are not themselves changed during the process of organization. And so we are able to understand why a cyclical dedifferentiation is necessary in highly evolved non-cellular organisms.

An analysis of the comparative morphology of ciliates has led to the conclusion that the period of predivision corresponds to a phylogenetically primitive structure, whether it is the pattern of kineties which is involved, or the position of some specialized systems. A non-cellular organism may therefore exhibit primitive and evolved features at different phases of its cycle. But as a matter of fact, changes are seen in the cortex only. Cortical events can not be anything else than the reflection of chemical changes controlled by enzymes and food. Nevertheless, the movements of cortical particles, because these particles are organized, can be understood only if the hypothesis of interactions between different types of associated particles is admitted. Any change in metabolism may bring about a rupture of an unstable equilibrium, the multiplication of some of the elements creating new poles of attraction, and an origination of new morphogenetic fields.

Let us quote here another of Paul Weiss's statements (1947): "No model of a cell can be pertinent unless it takes into account both the elementary processes and their organizational frame. Manifest cell organization results from the response of organized elements to fields of organized (i.e., non-random) physical and chemical conditions. . . ."

This statement, like the whole concept of "molecular ecology," may be applied directly to ciliates. Molecular ecology was a purely theoretical concept. The study of the dynamic aspects of kinetosomes during ontogeny and phylogeny of ciliates illustrates the importance of self-reproducing particles in developmental phenomena.

This study also shows the importance of cortical structure in organization and finally leads to a hypothesis concerning the interaction of the different building blocks which may throw some light on the problems of division and differentiation and on the mysterious fact that one single particle can exhibit so many types of activity.

"Life," Louis Pasteur has written, "is dominated by asymmetrical actions. I even foresee that all living species in their structures, in their external forms, are primordially functions of the cosmic dissymmetry."

The problems of the physicochemical aspects of organization and of asymmetry have been extensively discussed by E. Fauré-Frémiet (1943, 1948b) in suggestive reviews to which the reader should refer. Fauré-Frémiet has clearly considered the possibility of protoplasmic dissymmetry as the initial factor of orientation and has posed the question: "Are the spatial properties of an organized system determined by the anisotropic properties of molecules, or is the orientation of molecular structure controlled by distinct organizational factors?" The cell is a collection of molecules—micelles and organelles. The environment of a particle is essentially the sum of other particles, and one can question whether their spatial distribution, which is organization, is not the result of the interaction of the particles themselves. The morphogenetical field would be the reflection of the properties and relative number of these particles. Orienting forces would be the interplay of asymmetrical molecules.

For example, the peritrichous ciliate *Trichodina domerguei* possesses a circular adhesive organ. This organ is formed of articulated skeletal pieces of protein nature. After the division, a new ring is formed. The skeletal proteins are organized in a localized zone which behaves, according to E. Fauré-Frémiet and J. Thaureaux (1944), as a polymerization zone. In the formation of skeletal pieces, there is a given orientation, a given direction, an asymmetrical increase, the result of which is a specific organic structure. The properties of such a polymerization zone are those of a morphogenetic field.

The mechanist is intimately convinced that a precise knowledge of the chemical constitution, structure, and properties of the various organelles of a cell will solve biological problems. This will come in a few centuries. For the time being, the biologist has to face such concepts as orienting forces or morphogenetic fields. Owing to the scarcity of chemical data and to the complexity of life, and despite the progresses of biochemistry, the biologist is still threatened with vertigo. That is why such clear models as the formation of the skeletal pieces of a trichodine are very comforting and useful.

Unfortunately, most of the constituent parts of the cell are of submicroscopical size. Therefore special attention has to be given to the rare visible particles, especially to those visible particles endowed with genetic continuity. Such is the kinetosome.

Considering the history of protozoology, it may at first sight seem strange that so many nature lovers of the old times have been enchanted by ciliates. Of course, watching a ciliate stopping in his search for food to look at you through the microscope is most stirring. But my impression is that the lover of ciliates always had a presentiment that ciliates were to be the proving ground for visible self-reproducing particles. This is how and why we have considered ciliates.

# Bibliography

The bibliography is divided into two parts:

1. A list of quoted papers among which the most important, including general discussions, are indicated by an asterisk (*).
2. A list of books or papers which, owing to the scope of the book, have not been quoted or discussed but which are relevant to the subject.

## QUOTED PAPERS AND BOOKS


* BALAMUTH, W. 1940. Regeneration in Protozoa: a problem of morphogenesis. *Quart. Rev. Biol., 15*:290–337.

——. 1942. Studies on the organization of ciliate Protozoa: II. Reorganization processes in *Licnophora macfarlandi* during binary fission and regeneration. *J. Exp. Zool., 91*:15–43.

CASPARI, E. 1948. Cytoplasmic inheritance. *Advances in Genetics, 2*:1–66.

CHATTON, E. 1921. Réversion de la scission chez les Ciliés. Réalisation d'individus distomes et polyénergides de *Glaucoma scintillans* se multipliant indéfiniment par scissiparité. *Compt. rend. acad. sci., 173*:393–397.

——. 1924. Sur les connexions flagellaires des éléments flagellés. Centrosomes et mastigosomes. La cinétide, unité cinéto-flagellaire. Cinétides simples et cinétides composées. *Compt. rend. soc. biol., 91*:577–581.

——. 1931. Essai d'un schéma de l'énergide d'après une image objective et synthétique: le Dinoflagellé *Polykrikos Schwartzi* Bütschli. *Compt. rend. XIème Congrès International de Zoologie, Padova,* 169–187, pl. III–IV.

CHATTON, E., and S. BRACHON. 1935. Discrimination, chez deux Infusoires du genre *Glaucoma,* entre système argentophile et infraciliature. *Compt. rend. soc. biol., 118*:399.

* CHATTON, E., and A. LWOFF. 1935a. Les Ciliés apostomes. I. Aperçu historique et général; étude monographique des genres et des espèces. *Arch. zool. exp. et gén., 77*:1–453, 21 pl., 217 fig.

* Chatton, E., and A. Lwoff. 1935b. La constitution primitive de la strie ciliaire des infusoires. La desmodexie. *Compt. rend. soc. biol., 118*:1068–1072.

——. 1936. La division et la continuité du cinétome chez l'Ancistrumidé *Proboveria loripedis, n.g., n. sp.*, de *Loripes lacteus. Arch. zool. exp. et gén., 78, N. et R.*:84–91.

——. 1949. Recherches sur les Ciliés thigmotriches. *Arch. zool. exp. et gén., 86*:169–253.

Chatton, E., A. Lwoff, and M. Lwoff. 1929. Les infraciliatures et la continuité génétique des systèmes ciliaires récessifs. *Compt. rend. acad. sci., 188*:1190–1192.

——. 1931a. L'infraciliature de l'Infusoire Thigmotriche *Sphenophrya dosiniæ* (Ch. et Lw.). Structure, topographie, et développement. *Compt. rend. soc. biol., 107*:532–535.

——. 1931b. L'origine infraciliaire et la genèse des trichocystes et des trichites chez les Ciliés *Foettingeriidæ. Comp. rend. acad. sci., 193*:670–673.

Chatton, E., A. Lwoff, M. Lwoff, and J. Monod. 1931. La formation de l'ébauche buccale postérieure chez les Ciliés en division et ses relations de continuité avec la bouche antérieure. *Compt. rend. soc. biol., 107*:540–544.

Chatton, E., A. Lwoff, M. Lwoff, and L. Tellier. 1929. L'infraciliature et la continuité génétique des blépharoplastes chez l'Acinétien *Podophrya fixa* O. F. Müller. *Compt. rend. soc. biol., 100*:1191–1196.

Chatton, E., A. Lwoff, and L. Rapkine. 1931. L'apparition de groupements SH avant la division chez les *Foettingeriidæ* (Ciliés). *Compt. rend. soc. biol., 106*:626–629.

Chatton, E., and J. Seguela. 1940. La continuité génétique des formations ciliaires chez les Ciliés hypotriches. Le cinétome et l'argyrome au cours de la division. *Bull. biol. France-Belgique, 74*: 349–442.

Cohen, A. L. 1942. The organization of protoplasm: a possible experimental approach. *Growth, 6*:259–272.

Darlington, C. D. 1939. *The Evolution of Genetic Systems.* University Press, Cambridge.

——. 1944. Heredity, development, and infection. *Nature, Lond., 154*:164–169.

Dembowska, W. 1938. Körperreorganisation von *Stylonychia mytilus* beim Hungern. *Arch. f. Protistenk., 91*:89–105.

Dobell, C. C. 1911. The principles of protistology. *Arch. f. Protistenk., 23*:269–310.

* Fauré-Frémiet, E. 1943. Le problème de l'organisation et ses aspects physicochimiques. *Revue scientifique, fasc. 9*:433–446.

* Fauré-Frémiet, E. 1945a. *Podophrya parasitica,* nov. sp. *Bull. biol. France-Belgique, 79*:85.

*——. 1945b. Symétrie et polarité chez les ciliés bi- ou multicomposites. *Bull. biol. France-Belgique, 79*:106–150.

*——. 1948a. Doublets homopolaires et régulation morphogénétique chez le cilié *Leucophrys patula. Arch. anat. microscop. et morphol. exp., 37*:183–203.

*——. 1948b. Les mécanismes de la morphogenèse chez les ciliés. *Folia Biotheoretica, 111*:25–58.

Fauré-Frémiet, E., and H. Mugard. 1948. Ségrégation d'un matériel cortical au cours de la segmentation chez l'œuf de *Teredo norvegica. Compt. rend. acad. sci., 227*:1409–1411.

* Fauré-Frémiet, E., and J. Thaureaux. 1944. Protéines de structure et cytosquelette chez les Urcéolarides. *Bull. biol. France-Belgique, 78*:143–156.

* Harrison, R. G. 1937. Embryology and its relations. *Science, 85*:369–374.

Huxley, J. S., and G. R. de Beer. 1934. *The Elements of Experimental Embryology.* University Press, Cambridge.

Just, E. E. 1939. *The Biology of the Cell Surface.* P. Blakiston, Philadelphia.

Lwoff, A. 1944. *L'évolution physiologique. Etude des pertes de fonctions chez les microorganismes.* Hermann, Paris.

——. 1949a. Discussion du rapport Sonneborn et Beale. In Colloque *Unités biologiques douées de continuité génétique.* Centre National de la Recherche Scientifique, Paris, p. 35.

*——. 1949b. Les organites doués de continuité génétique chez les protistes. In Colloque *Unités biologiques douées de continuité génétique.* Centre National de la Recherche Scientifique, Paris.

Lwoff, A., and H. Dusi. 1935. La suppression expérimentale des chloroplastes chez *Euglena mesnili. Compt. rend. soc. biol., 119*:1092.

Monod, J. 1947. Enzymatic adaptation, its bearing on problems of genetics and cellular differentiation. *Growth Symposium, 11*:223–289.

Mugard, H. 1947. Division et morphogenèse chez les Ophryoglènes. *Compt. rend. acad. sci., 225*:70–72.

Schmitt, F. O. 1941. Some protein patterns in cells. *Growth Symposium, 5*:1–20.

Sinnott, E. W. 1939. The cell-organ relationship in plant organization. *Growth, 3*:77–86.

Sonneborn, T. M., and G. H. Beale. 1949. Influence des gènes, des plasmagènes, et du milieu dans le déterminisme des caractères antigéniques chez *Paramecium aurelia* (variété 4). In Colloque *Unités biologiques douées de continuité génétique.* Centre National de la Recherche Scientifique, Paris.

* TARTAR, V. 1941. Intracellular patterns: facts and principles concerning patterns exhibited in the morphogenesis and regeneration of ciliate protozoa. *Growth, 5*:23.

VILLENEUVE-BRACHON, S. 1940. Recherches sur les ciliés hétérotriches. *Arch. zool. exp. et gén., 82*:1–180.

WEISS, P. 1947. The problem of specificity in growth and development. *Yale J. Biol. and Med., 19*:235–278.

WEISS, P. 1949. Differential growth. In *Chemistry and Physiology of Growth,* edited by A. K. Parpart. Princeton University Press.

WHITAKER, D. M. 1940. Physical factors of growth. *Growth, 4*:75–90.

WRIGHT, S. 1941. The physiology of the gene. *Physiol. Rev., 21*:487–527.

## RELEVANT BOOKS AND PAPERS

ASTBURY, W. T. 1945. The forms of biological molecules. In *Essays on Growth and Form.* Clarendon Press.

BERRILL, N. J. 1941. Spatial and temporal growth patterns in colonial organisms. *Growth, 5*:89–111.

BLAKESLEE, A. F. 1941. Growth patterns in plants. *Growth, 5*:77–88.

HARRISON, R. G. Cellular differentiation and internal environment. *Amer. Assoc. Adv. Science,* no. 14:77–97.

——. 1945. Relations of symmetry in the developing embryo. *Trans. Conn. Acad. Arts and Sciences, 36*:277–330.

RAPER, K. B. 1941. Developmental patterns in simple slime molds. *Growth, 5*:69–74.

TYLER, A. 1947. An auto-antibody concept of cell structure, growth, and differentiation. *Growth Symposium,* 7–19.

WEISS, P. 1939. *Principles of Development.* Henry Holt, New York.

——. 1949. Differential growth. In *Chemistry and Physiology of Growth,* edited by A. K. Parpart. Princeton University Press.

WRIGHT, S. 1945. Genes as physiological agents. General considerations. *Amer. Nat., 79*:289–303.

# Index